Ainsi

To Ewan

Max et
les tittes

Dominique de Saint Mars

Serge Bloch

© CALLIGRAM

CHRISTIAN ⊙ GALLIMARD

*Avec la collaboration
de Renaud de Saint Mars*

Merci au Service pour la promotion
de l'égalité du canton de Genève
pour leurs conseils.

Série dirigée par Dominique de Saint Mars

© Calligram 2000
Tous droits réservés pour tous pays
Imprimé en Italie
ISBN : 978-2-88445-559-6

Et tu ne pourras plus sortir, je t'attends derrière la porte !

MAX, je t'interdis !

Mais, maîtresse, Bérénice ne fait que nous embêter !

Et voilà, elle va encore le croire...

... et encore dire que c'est les filles qui commencent !

DRINNNNNG !!!

En rang et on se calme !

T'entends ? On se calme !

Mon chouchou, rends-le moi !

Tu dis que tu me le donnes et tu le reprends !

Bah, les filles, ça n'a pas de parole, on commence à le savoir.

Bérénice et Fathia !

T'es vraiment pénible, Max !

8

9

* Attitude méprisante à l'égard du sexe féminin.

12

Bon, pour se calmer, on va parler des métiers que vous voudriez faire plus tard...

Moi, je veux être pilote de course !

Et moi, pilote d'avion !

TSSS, TSSS, moi, je ne monterai jamais dans ton avion !

Parce que je suis une fille ?

Moi, je veux être policier ! Enfin... policière !

Et moi, chirurgienne...

13

14

Mais c'est intéressant, les différences...
Dans la nature, les femelles organisent tout pour
la sécurité de leurs petits et la survie de l'espèce.
Elles sont prévoyantes...

Chez les éléphants,
c'est la vieille mère qui
conduit le
troupeau !

Et les mâles, par leur nature de chasseur,
partent loin, prennent des risques, agissent
vite et fort. Et ils sont toujours
un peu en compétition...

Ah ! Ah ! C'est pour ça
qu'ils ont toujours besoin
de frimer un peu !!!

Chez les lions,
c'est la lionne qui
chasse...

Mais, Fathia,
c'est le lion qui
découpe !

Mais notre culture* a changé. Maintenant les femmes votent et rapportent aussi la nourriture.

À part les bébés et les travaux de force... les hommes et les femmes peuvent faire les mêmes choses, avec une sensibilité différente.

AH, VOUS VOYEZ !

* Ensemble des manières de vivre et des idées d'une société, d'un peuple.

16

* Adjectif espagnol (se prononce *matcho*) désignant quelqu'un qui pense que l'homme a le droit d'être le maître de la femme.

20

23

24

25

27

Pour nous avoir un nombre incalculable de fois tiré les cheveux, bourrées de coups de pied... pour nous avoir tout autant soulevé nos jupes, tiré nos pantalons, traitées de boudins...

... de thons, de grosses nulles, de mammouths... pour nous avoir obligées à obéir, espionnées aux toilettes, empêchées de parler, ridiculisées en classe...

... piétinant ainsi les droits élémentaires d'une moitié de l'humanité...

29

31

QUOI, vous ne venez pas ?

Je n'aurais pas dû les abandonner. Elles sont plus nombreuses... Elles vont les torturer !

33

34

36

* La Convention internationale des droits de l'enfant donne des droits égaux à tout enfant sans distinction de race, de couleur, de sexe, de langue, de religion, d'opinion politique.

38

Et toi...

Est-ce qu'il t'est arrivé la même histoire qu'à Max?
Réponds aux deux questionnaires...

Ils te tapent, t'insultent, te font peur? Te laisses-tu faire?
Te défends-tu? ou les trouves-tu plus gentils que les filles?

Ça te révolte ou ça t'amuse s'ils soulèvent ta jupe?
Sais-tu dire non si tu ne le veux pas? À qui en parles-tu?

En classe, se moquent-ils de toi? Te sens-tu sans intérêt,
invisible? Préfères-tu te taire, obéir et travailler plus?

40

Y a-t-il des métiers que tu aimerais faire plus tard,
mais qui sont d'après toi des métiers d'homme?

Chez toi, vois-tu souvent ton père faire la vaisselle
et ta mère lire le journal, assise dans un fauteuil?

Sais-tu que dans certains pays les filles vont moins à l'école
que les garçons, car elles doivent travailler pour la maison?

Pourquoi le fais-tu? Pour imiter tes copains? Penses-tu
que les filles en ont envie? ou tu ne les embêtes pas?

Es-tu curieux du corps des filles? Tu ne sais pas comment
les approcher autrement qu'en les bousculant?

Elles t'embêtent, se moquent de toi, te font peur?
En souffres-tu? ou sont-elles gentilles avec toi?

As-tu de l'énergie et envie de te battre ou bien tu n'aimes pas ça? T'arrive-t-il de pleurer, d'être traité de fille?

Penses-tu que c'est mieux d'être un garçon ou une fille? Chez toi, on t'apprend le respect, ou pas? Le dit-on chez toi?

Penses-tu que les filles peuvent faire les mêmes métiers que les garçons? qu'un père doit aussi s'occuper de son bébé?

**Après avoir réfléchi
à ces questions
sur les garçons et les filles,
tu peux en parler
avec tes parents ou tes amis.**

Dans la même collection

Application Max et Lili
disponible sur

App Store
Google play

www.editionscalligram.ch

Suivez notre actualité sur Facebook
https://www.facebook.com/MaxEtLili

DOCTO
AND THE
OF THE

DOCTOR WHO
AND THE TERROR
OF THE AUTONS

Based on the BBC television serial *Doctor Who and
the Terror of the Autons* by Robert Holmes by arrangement with the British Broadcasting Corporation.

TERRANCE DICKS

Illustrated by Alan Willow

A TARGET BOOK
published by
the Paperback Division of
W. H. Allen & Co. Ltd

A Target Book
Published in 1975
by the Paperback Division of W. H. Allen & Co. Ltd
A Howard & Wyndham Company
44 Hill Street, London W1X 8LB

Second impression 1979
Third impression 1980

Printed in Great Britain by
The Anchor Press Ltd
Tiptree, Essex

ISBN 0 426 11500 7

Contents

The Terror Begins

Luigi Rossini came down the steps of his caravan and looked about him with satisfaction. Most people wouldn't have seen much cause for pleasure—a tatty little circus setting up in a muddy field. But Luigi Rossini, who had been born Lew Ross in Hoxton fifty years ago, saw things differently. The wagons and caravans might be worn and shabby, the elephants old and tired, the lions and tigers mangy—but the Circus Rossini was *his*. He was the Boss. And that was what Luigi Rossini enjoyed.

The little circus never made very much money. It was too small to book the profitable sites, and had to be content with little village greens and shabby suburban recreation grounds. But Rossini had his own way of making money. He hired only the deadbeats, the down-and-outs of the circus profession; those who for one reason or another could never get a job with the big, posh outfits. Some were too old, or too incompetent. Some, like Tony the strong man, were on the run from the police. Rossini hired them all, and paid them starvation wages, knowing they wouldn't dare to ask for more. All the profits went into his own pockets, paying for the flashy suits, the diamond rings and the big cigars that fitted Rossini's picture of himself as an international showman. Anyone who objected was soon beaten into submission by Rossini's big fists. He had a right to his perks. He was the boss, wasn't he?

Things were looking particularly good this week. One of the bigger circuses had been closed down by 'flu and, by a bit of quick moving, Rossini had been able to take up their booking. For once, the Circus Rossini had a decent pitch, a nice little field on the outskirts of a fair sized market town. There was every chance of a good crowd when they opened up in the morning; a decent few quid in the kitty for once. Not that it would make any difference to the rest of the circus folk. But Luigi Rossini was already thinking about a new car. One of those nice big American jobs—a Cadillac or a Chevrolet.

Rossini produced a big cigar, lit it with a flourish, and prepared to start bullying his crew to get a move on. They'd have the big top up and the seats prepared before any of them stopped for food or rest. Naturally that didn't apply to the Boss. After he'd got them all toiling, he'd go back to his luxurious caravan and demolish a cold chicken and most of a bottle of whisky.

Suddenly Rossini heard a strange noise. A sort of wheezing, groaning, mechanical sound. It seemed to come from the furthest corner of the field. There, under the shade of a few trees, was parked the horse-box which held Madame Mariella's Prancing Ponies—three worn out old nags who could hardly manage a gallop, let alone a prance. To his astonishment, Rossini saw that another horse-box was parked beside it. But this was a horse-box of a very different sort, glossy and gleaming, brand spanking new. The sort of horse-box to carry Derby winners to the racecourse. But what was it doing in his field? Why hadn't he seen it drive in? Angrily, Rossini strode towards it.

He peered suspiciously into the driver's cab. It was empty. Rossini marched round to the back and hammered on the rear doors. But as soon as his fist touched the door, he snatched it back in dismay. The horse-box *tingled*. He felt a hum of suppressed power, almost like an electric shock. The rear door snapped open and a man stood looking at him.

Rossini saw a man of medium height, dressed in neat dark clothing. He had a rather sallow face with a small

8

pointed beard, heavy eyebrows and dark burning eyes. With a sudden flash of superstitious fear, Rossini thought the stranger looked like the Devil.

Rossini took a grip of himself. No funny-looking foreigner was going to frighten him. He was Luigi Rossini—the Boss. He scowled up at the man angrily. 'Who the heck are you?'

The stranger came down the horse-box steps. He spoke in a deep voice, full of authority. 'I am usually referred to as the Master.'

Rossini sneered. 'Is that so?'

The Master smiled as if at a private joke. 'Universally!'

'Well, I'm Luigi Rossini, and I'm the boss round here. So get off my pitch while you're still safe.'

The Master's dark eyes seemed to blaze suddenly with anger. 'You insolent primitive!'

Despite himself, Rossini took a step back. Then he too became angry. 'All right, so you want it the hard way.' Rossini reached out to grab the intruder. The Master's hands flashed out and clamped round his wrists. The big man struggled but found himself utterly helpless. It was as though his wrists were set in concrete. He looked at the Master's face, and immediately his glance was caught by those deep burning eyes. They seemed to grow larger and larger, swallowing up Rossini's whole brain. He heard the deep voice changing, 'I am the Master. You will obey me!'

The Master bore down, and Rossini was forced to his knees. For a moment longer the Master held him, gazing deep into his eyes. Then satisfied, he released Rossini's wrists and stepped back. He snapped his fingers once, sharply, like a pistol shot. Then he turned and walked towards Rossini's caravan. Rossini scrambled to his feet and followed, trailing dog-like at the heels of the Master.

*　　*　　*　　*　　*

The room housing the special meteorite exhibition at the National Science Museum was almost empty. It was nearly closing time, and most of the visitors were already making for the exits. Two men lingered by one of the special display cases. One was big and bulky, the other a neat, dark man with a little beard. He seemed fascinated by the case's contents, though there was nothing very spectacular to see, just an army ammunition box, the lid propped open. Inside the box, on a nest of straw, stood a sphere, roughly the size of a football, made of some dull, dark green material. The caption card in the case said the sphere was part of a freak meteor shower that had fallen in southern England, and drew attention to the unusual regularity of its shape. As he read the card, the smaller of the two men smiled to himself, and stroked his neat pointed beard.

The Master looked at his watch. It was five fifty-eight, two minutes to closing time. He stepped back, shielded his eyes with his left hand while his gloved right hand swept forward in a single slashing blow. The heavy glass case disintegrated in a shower of tiny fragments. The Master leaned forward, closed the ammunition box and tucked it under his arm. A museum guard ran into the room, and stopped in outraged astonishment. 'Here, what do you think you're . . .' Rossini stepped up behind him and smashed him to the ground. The Master gave a little nod of satisfaction, tucked the box under his arm, and walked briskly towards the exit.

*　　*　　*　　*　　*

As Jo Grant walked along the corridors of UNIT H.Q. she was bubbling over with an uneasy mixture of excitement and apprehension. At last she had achieved her ambition. She was a fully fledged member of UNIT, the United Nations Intelligence Taskforce. The fact that she was the newest and most junior member of that top-secret organisation did nothing to spoil her pleasure. But on the other hand she was about to meet the Doctor, and the thought of the coming encounter was enough to give her a mild attack of the shakes.

Still, she consoled herself, she'd felt much the same way before meeting Brigadier Lethbridge-Stewart, and he couldn't have been kinder. Jo was well aware that she owed her appointment to some discreet wire-pulling by her uncle, who, luckily for her, happened to be a Cabinet Minister. She'd been afraid that the Brigadier might resent this, but the Brigadier had seemed genuinely pleased to see her. Not only that, he'd given her a top job on her very first day. Jo had quite expected to start at the bottom, making tea, filing reports and running errands. But, to her delight and astonishment, her interview with the Brigadier had ended very differently.

Once the impressive ceremony of reading and signing the Official Secrets Act was over, the Brigadier had said, 'That concludes the formalities, Miss Grant. You can start work immediately. You will be the Doctor's new assistant.'

Even now Jo was hardly over the shock. Assistant to the Doctor, UNIT's mysterious Scientific Adviser! She had tried to stammer out her thanks, but the Brigadier had waved them aside. 'Don't thank me, Miss Grant. You haven't met the Doctor yet!' And with these rather ominous words the Brigadier had given her an envelope to hand to the Doctor, told her where to find the laboratory, and bustled her from his office. There had been something almost amused in his manner . . .

Jo found herself standing outside the laboratory door. She braced herself, drew herself up to her full five feet, and tapped timidly on the door. No reply. She tapped again. Still nothing. Cautiously, she opened the door a crack, and peered into the room.

She got a quick, confused impression of a spacious room with a big window along the far side. There were several laboratory benches, all covered with an elaborate tangle of scientific apparatus. In one corner stood the incongruous shape of a battered old police box. Perched on a stool at one of the benches was a very tall man with a shock of white hair. Before him on the bench lay a complex piece of electronic circuitry, and he was making careful adjustments to it with a strangely shaped instrument. As Jo watched, he sat back for a moment, rubbing his chin thoughtfully. Then, leaning forward again, he made one more careful adjustment. The results were immediate and spectacular. The electronic circuit began to glow, turning a fierce cherry-red.

Jo Grant might have been inexperienced, but she knew how to cope with an emergency. On the wall nearby was a fire extinguisher. She grabbed it from its bracket and dashed into the laboratory.

Watched by the Doctor, the piece of apparatus was still glowing fiercely. Jo rapped the extinguisher on the floor to start it and squirted a jet of white foam on to the circuit. There was a bang and a flash, and the apparatus belched a cloud of dense black smoke. The Doctor caught the full blast and doubled up coughing and choking. Jo reached up and thumped him between the shoulder blades. He straightened up, and peered through smoke-reddened eyes at his piece of apparatus. 'It's all right,' said Jo kindly. 'No need to worry, I've dealt with it.'

The Doctor looked at the bench, where his experiment was completely buried beneath a little pyramid of sticky white foam. Grimly he rolled up his sleeves and plunged his hands into the foam, extracting a charred and sticky tangle of blackened circuitry. 'Dealt with it? You've ruined it!'

Jo was indignant. 'You're just overflowing with gratitude, aren't you? This whole place might have gone up.'

The Doctor was blowing the remnants of fire extinguisher foam from his ruined circuit. 'My dear young lady, steady-state micro-welding always creates intense heat. It's perfectly safe. You've ruined three months' delicate work. Now then, may I ask who you are?'

Jo sighed. 'My name's Jo Grant,' she said resignedly. 'I'm your new assistant.'

The Doctor looked down at her in speechless astonishment. He saw a very small, very pretty girl with fair hair and blue eyes, who looked as if she should still be at school. She seemed almost on the point of tears. 'I'm sorry, my dear,' he said gently. 'I really don't think you'd be suitable.'

'I'm a fully trained agent,' said Jo eagerly. 'I've just finished the training course. Codes, safe-breaking, explosives . . .'

The Doctor's face broke into a suddenly youthful smile.

'Fire fighting?' he added gently.

Jo looked so crestfallen that the Doctor couldn't help feeling sorry for her.

'You see,' he explained, 'I really need a very experienced scientist, someone who could help me in my work.'

'I took "O" level in science . . .'

The Doctor shook his head firmly. 'I'm sorry, my dear. Now if you'll excuse me, I've got a great deal to do.' The Doctor started the laborious job of sorting out the tangle of blackened wires in front of him.

Jo remembered the Brigadier's envelope and fished it out from her pocket. 'The Brigadier wanted me to give you this report.'

The Doctor was still absorbed in his work. 'Well, what's it about?'

'I don't know.'

'Then open it and tell me!'

Hurriedly, Jo tore open the envelope and extracted a

memo. She skimmed through it quickly. 'Seems to be about a robbery. Something stolen from the National Science Museum . . . It was on loan from this H.Q. . . .'

'What does he think I am,' grumbled the Doctor, 'a policeman? *What* was stolen?'

'A small green sphere, about the size of a football. Some kind of meteorite . . .'

The Doctor's reaction was electric. He sat bolt upright on his stool and snapped, 'The Nestene energy unit? It should never have been allowed to leave this building!'

Jo looked again at the memo. 'Apparently the museum people wanted it for some kind of special exhibition. The Brigadier gave his permission . . .'

The Doctor reached out a long arm and twitched the memo from her fingers. He read through it rapidly, then threw it down angrily on the bench. 'The Brigadier must be out of his mind. I knew I should have destroyed the thing. Somehow it seemed too much like murder.'

Jo looked at him in astonishment. 'Murder? You mean the thing was alive?'

'Most definitely. Still dormant, but alive. It was the container for a form of alien intelligence.'

'You've just got to be joking.'

The Doctor said grimly, 'There's precious little to joke about, I assure you. That thing's appallingly dangerous.'

Briefly the Doctor told Jo the story of the first Nestene invasion. He told her of the Nestenes themselves, strange malevolent octopus-like creatures with an affinity for plastic. They had the power to divest themselves of their own bodies and create new ones. 'You mean they can make plastic come to life?' asked Jo incredulously.

The Doctor nodded. 'Anything plastic, anything at all, can become a vehicle for the Nestene consciousness.' He went on to tell Jo how the Nestenes had come to Earth, their 'consciousness' encased in the plastic globes that had at first been taken for meteorites. Through

14

their agent, Channing, they had taken over a plastics factory and built the terrifying Autons, man-like killer automatons. He told of the chaos when the Autons, disguised as shop window dummies, came to life all over England, stalking through the streets and blasting down everyone they met. Finally he told her of the last battle at the plastics factory, when a giant Nestene 'grown' by Channing in a huge tank had burst forth in its own terrifying form, only to be destroyed by the Doctor's specially built UHF transmitter. 'They'd poured almost the whole of their consciousness into that monster,' explained the Doctor. 'All that was on Earth, anyway. When I destroyed it, they were all destroyed. The shock was transmitted telepathically to the other units.'

'What about the one that was stolen—the one in the museum?'

'After it was all over I got the Brigadier and his men to make a final search of the area where the Nestenes had first landed. They found just one more globe, still dormant. It had never been collected and activated like the others.'

Jo looked puzzled. 'If it is so dangerous, why did you keep it?'

The Doctor grinned wryly. 'You might say as a sort of barometer. I ran a check on it from to time. You see, if the Nestenes came to Earth, the unit would have become active again. It would have given us a bit of warning. Now it's gone.'

'You don't *know* there's any connection with what happened before,' argued Jo. 'Maybe it was just some idiot souvenir hunter.'

The Doctor was dubious. 'Let's hope so.'

'Of course it was,' said Jo optimistically. 'Why else would anyone steal it? What *use* would it be?'

The Doctor rubbed his chin thoughtfully. Jo could see that he was really worried. 'It's possible,' he said slowly, 'that someone's stolen it for a purpose. Stolen it with a view to activating it. If they succeed, they could open a channel for a second Nestene invasion!'

2

Sabotage at the Space Probe

Albert Goodge, a melancholy, balding, bespectacled scientist, drove slowly and cautiously as always along the narrow country lane, plunged in his usual gloom and lost to the beauty of the scene around him. It was a fine day in early summer. Fields and hedges lay bathed in sunshine, birds sang, lambs gambolled; and Albert Goodge worried about the quality of his packed lunch. He turned a corner, and DSRC 2, Deep Space Research Centre No. 2, lay spread before him.

It was an incongruous sight in the quiet stretch of English countryside, but the centre had a strange beauty all its own. The long slender tower, crowned with the searching antennae of the radio telescope, stretched upwards into the blue sky, the main control buildings nestling around its base. Goodge drove to the gates and into the car park. He got out of the car, crossed to the base of the tower, and, lunch box under his arm, started climbing the seemingly endless steps to the little sub-control cabin that was built into the top of the tower, just under the antennae of the telescope.

A few minutes later he puffed his way into the cabin, where everything seemed quiet and normal. Professor Phillips was sitting at the control console, taking the routine readings that marked the end of his shift. Goodge looked at him gloomily. He didn't approve of young Phillips. Another of these whizz-kids straight from university. Phillips registered Goodge's entrance and spoke without taking his eyes from his clipboard. 'All yours in a moment, old chap.'

Goodge sighed and opened his lunch box. His worst fears were confirmed. Eggs again!

'I told her only last night,' he said indignantly.

Phillips went on taking readings. 'Mmm?'

' "Cut out the boiled eggs, Elsie," I said. "Quite apart from the effect on my digestion they're boring to look at." '

'Aha!' said Professor Phillips, who hadn't heard a word of all this. Goodge was always grumbling about something, and most of his colleagues had stopped listening long ago.

'When you've seen one boiled egg, you've seen them all. Eggs are *boring!* Don't you agree, Professor?'

'Never thought about it,' said Phillips. He closed his notebook and Goodge slid into the empty seat and automatically began checking the rows of monitor dials. Philips paused by the door and looked back at his colleague. All around them instruments whirred and clicked. Radio pulses and emissions from the depths of deep space were being monitored and recorded by the giant radio telescope, checked on the computer in an attempt to detect a pattern, a meaning, some clue to the biggest question of all. Was there, somewhere in the galaxy, an intelligence other than man? Here in this tiny cabin they were listening to the voices of the stars. And old Goodge was grumbling about boiled eggs! Phillips shook his head and left the cabin. Closing the door behind him, he started clattering down the metal steps on his way to the main control area.

Albert Goodge, still obsessed with boiled eggs, continued the routine duties that marked the beginning of his shift on the scanner. Above his head, a sort of skylight was set into the roof of the cabin. Had Goodge looked up, he might have caught a glimpse of a dark shape peering down at him. He might even have been able to sound the alarm in time to save his own life. But he didn't look up.

On the roof of the cabin the Master lay spreadeagled like some giant bat. He had been there since before dawn, waiting with icy patience for the right moment. Now it was here. He slid from the roof, dropped nimbly onto the catwalk outside it, and flinging open the door, stepped inside the little cabin.

Goodge swung round as the door was opened, assuming that Phillips had forgotten something. He caught a quick glimpse of a bearded man in the doorway, covering him with a squat, oddly shaped gun. There was a crackle of power and Goodge felt as if his whole body was being clamped in a giant fist and squeezed, squeezed. He seemed to be shrinking, rushing down the wrong end of a telescope into blackness.

In the main control area, Professor Phillips was punching his results into a computer and studying the read-out screen. All around him instruments hummed as normal.

In the little sub-control cabin, the Master snapped shut the lid of Goodge's lunch box, a slight smile on his lips. He opened the UNIT ammunition box and took out the dull green sphere. From inside his coat he produced what appeared to be some kind of connecting device, a length of cable with terminals at each end. One terminal he attached to the sphere, the other he plugged into the radio telescope itself. Then in a blur of speed his hands began flickering over the controls. There was a steady hum of rising power. The dull green sphere seemed to come to life. It began to glow and pulse with a greenish light, dimly at first then brighter and brighter. The hum of power within the cabin rose to an almost unendurable shriek . . .

A dark shape peered down at him

Phillips in main control suddenly became aware that something was badly wrong. His instruments too were humming with increased power. The dials and scanners around him juddered wildly. He switched on the intercom. 'Goodge! What's going on? Have you gone crazy up there?' There was no reply. Phillips yelled, 'The digital shaft-angle encoder's gone crazy. Check the feedback control!' There was no reply. Phillips ran out of main control and headed for the tower.

The power surge in the sub-control cabin rose to a crescendo and then cut out. There was a sudden, unearthly silence. The Master smiled. The transmission was complete. In its box the Nestene energy unit was blazing and crackling with exultant life. The Master smiled, and shut the lid of the ammunition box. The door of the cabin opened, and Phillips dashed in angrily. 'Goodge, what the devil . . .' He broke off as the Master turned to face him. 'Where's Goodge?' Phillips demanded. 'Who the blazes are you?'

The Master advanced purposefully towards him, his eyes blazing with authority. 'Allow me to introduce myself. I am the Master.' The voice seemed to echo inside Phillip's head. 'I am the Master. You will obey me!'

A few minutes later, the Master, ammunition box under his arm, walked quickly down the steps of the tower. Professor Phillips followed behind him. They walked to the car park, got into Phillips' car and drove away.

*   *   *   *   *

The Doctor and the Brigadier were engaged in one of their not infrequent arguments. Good friends though they were, their temperaments were so utterly different that the occasional clash was inevitable. This time the subject of dispute was the missing Nestene energy unit. The Brigadier, aware that he should never have allowed it to go to the museum, knew that he was really in the wrong. As a result he was naturally insisting that he was completely in the right.

'Nonsense, Doctor! I will not give such a paltry matter a red priority. Normal routine enquiries will be carried out by the police.'

The Doctor took a deep breath. 'You, Brigadier, are the most stubborn, obstinate, pig-headed . . .'

'After all,' the Brigadier protested, 'you said yourself that it was inactive . . .'

'It may be inactive now. But we've no guarantee it will stay that way.'

The Doctor made a mighty effort to be diplomatic. 'You must believe me, Brigadier. It really is important.'

The Brigadier picked up a phone, dialled, and snapped, 'Sergeant Benton? UNIT will assist the civilian police in attempting to recover the missing energy unit. Set up liaison, will you? Oh, Benton, priority red one.' He slammed down the phone.

'Satisfied, Doctor?'

'Thank you very much, Brigadier,' said the Doctor acidly. 'Even though the horse has gone, we can still shut a stable door or two. Now, perhaps, I could ask you another favour?'

'What sort of favour?' enquired the Brigadier suspiciously.

'Keep that ridiculous child out of my hair. She's driving me mad.'

'Child? What child?'

The Doctor held out his hand about five feet above the ground. 'You know. The one who seems to think she's my assistant.'

'Miss Grant is scarcely a child, Doctor. And liaison with you happens to form the main part of her duties.'

'Then find her some new ones. I need a properly qualified scientist.'

The Brigadier's face took on a rather cunning expression. 'Very well, Doctor, I'll reassign her.' The Doctor gave a satisfied smile, which vanished at once as the Brigadier added, 'but I think you should break the news to her yourself.'

'Now just a minute,' protested the Doctor. Just then Jo rushed into the room, bubbling over with energy and enthusiasm.

'I've checked all the incoming reports, Doctor. Still nothing on the stolen energy unit. I've chased up the new electronic spares you need to start work on your new dematerialisition circuit. Supply says they'll most likely have to be flown in from Tokyo, but they'll make it a rush job. And is there anything else I can do?'

Having delivered all this more or less in one breath, Jo gazed appealingly up at the Doctor, looking, he thought, rather like a puppy desperately hoping someone will throw another stick. The Doctor braced himself to tell her that she was no longer to be his assistant. 'As a matter of fact, Miss Grant . . .'

His voice trailed away. He looked appealingly at the Brigadier. The Brigadier looked back impassively. The Doctor smiled down at Jo. 'Thank you very much, Miss Grant,' he said gently. 'I know you're going to be a great help to me.'

The corner of the Brigadier's mouth twitched, and the Doctor glared at him. Jo, unaware of all this byplay, turned back to the Brigadier, producing a despatch. 'Oh, and there's a message from one of our field sections, sir. Sabotage at a Deep Space Research Centre. Two men missing, and damage to the radio telescope.'

Before the Brigadier could react the Doctor said, 'Let me see that!' Taking the message from Jo he read through it rapidly, then grabbed his cloak from the peg in the corner, and swung it round his shoulders. 'I knew it!' he said with grim satisfaction. 'The theft of the energy unit was the first stage in some kind of plan!'

The Brigadier looked baffled. 'You think there's a connection between that and this radio telescope business?'

'Of course there is, man!'

Jo said, 'But how can you be so sure?'

'Because I've been waiting for something like this. First the energy unit goes, then there's trouble at a Research Centre dealing with Deep Space.' The Doctor opened the door and paused. 'Well? Are you two coming or not?'

*　　*　　*　　*　　*

Not very much later, Jo was holding on tight as the Doctor's funny little car shot down the narrow country lanes. For all her old-fashioned looks, 'Bessie', as the Doctor called her, had shown a surprising turn of speed on the journey down from London. Jo could still recall the expression on the face of a Jaguar driver as Bessie sped past him. Beside her, the Brigadier sat up stiffly in an attempt to preserve his dignity. He hated travelling in Bessie and was heartily glad when the Research Centre came into view, and they turned into the car park. Captain Yates, the Brigadier's young No. 2, was waiting to meet them. 'Everything's laid on, sir. The Director's waiting for you in Main Control.'

The Doctor swung his long legs over the side of the car. 'Is that where the trouble was?'

Yates shook his head. 'Not really, Doctor. Far as I can gather most of the dirty work took place up there.' Yates pointed at the little control cabin, perched high on the top of the tower.

'That's where I'll be then,' said the Doctor, and strode away towards the steps.

23

The Brigadier sighed, and followed by Jo and Captain Yates, went into the Main Control building to meet the Director.

The Doctor was far fitter than most human beings could ever be, but even he was glad of a rest by the time he reached the top of the seemingly endless flight of steps that led up to the sub-control cabin.

He found himself on the narrow platform outside the front door at last, and paused to take a few deep breaths. Then, just as he stretched his hand out to open the door a voice spoke in his ear. 'I shouldn't, Doctor. I really shouldn't.'

He spun round and saw a distinguished-looking elderly gentleman in the full rigout of a city businessman, dark suit, rolled umbrella and bowler hat. The peculiar thing was that the stranger was nonchalantly standing in thin air, hundreds of feet above the ground. The Doctor showed no particular surprise at this. Nor did the new arrival as he became aware of it. 'Dear me, my co-ordinates must have slipped a bit.' He blurred, shimmered out of existence and reappeared, standing next to the Doctor on the little platform.

The Doctor looked at him grimly. He'd recognised him at once, of course. One of the High Council of the Time Lords.

Last time they had met was at the Doctor's trial. After many years of happily wandering around the universe in his 'borrowed' TARDIS, the Doctor had been captured at last by his own people, and condemned to exile on the planet Earth for an indefinite period. But why had a Time Lord materialised himself here now? To give himself time to recover the Doctor said, 'May I say you look quite ridiculous in those clothes?'

The Time Lord gave a complacent smile. 'Merely merging with the natives, old chap. We Time Lords don't care to be conspicuous.' He shot a quick glance at the

24

Doctor's usual flamboyant outfit of narrow trousers, smoking jacket, frilled shirt and swirling cloak. 'Most of us, that is,' he added pointedly.

A hope flashed into the Doctor's mind. 'You've come to tell me the exile is over . . .'

The Time Lord shook his head. I'm afraid not, Doctor. As a matter of fact, I've come to bring you a warning. An old friend of yours has arrived on Earth.'

'One of our people? Who is it?'

The Time Lord pronounced a string of mellifluous syllables—one of the strange Time Lord names that are never disclosed to outsiders. Then he added, 'These days he calls himself the Master.'

The Doctor was silent for a moment. The Master was a rogue Time Lord. So too was the Doctor, in a way. But all *his* interventions in the course of history were on the side of good. The Master intervened only to cause death and suffering, usually in the pursuit of some scheme to seize power for himself. More than that, he seemed to delight in chaos and destruction for its own sake, and liked nothing more than to make a bad situation worse. Already he had been behind several Interplanetary Wars, always disappearing from the scene before he could be brought to justice. If ever he were caught, his fate would be far worse than the Doctor's exile. Once captured by the Time Lords, the Master's life-stream would be thrown into reverse. Not only would he no longer exist, he would never *have* existed. It was the severest punishment in the Time Lords' power.

The Doctor knew that the Master's presence on earth made matters far worse than he had feared. 'You're sure he's here?' he asked.

The Time Lord nodded gravely. 'We tracked him on the Monitor. Then there was some kind of alien interference and we lost contact.'

'Is his TARDIS still working?'

'I'm afraid so. He got away before it could be de-energised.'

'Then he was luckier than I,' said the Doctor sadly. He had never really got used to his exile.

'Don't be bitter, Doctor. Your punishment was comparatively light.'

The Doctor rounded on him angrily. 'Whatever I've done, I too am still a Time Lord. Do you know what it's like to be restricted to one tiny planet, one limited era of time?'

The Time Lord shrugged. 'It *is* your favourite planet after all!'

For a moment the Doctor gazed up at the summer sky without speaking. Then he said, 'Why did you take the trouble to warn me?'

'The Master knows you're on this planet, Doctor. You have interfered with his evil schemes in the past, and he has sworn your destruction. The Council felt you should be warned of your danger.'

The Doctor looked at him suspiciously. 'There's more to it than that, isn't there?'

The Time Lord paused, choosing his words carefully. 'You and the Master will inevitably come into conflict. If in the process he should be captured or destroyed . . .'

'I see. You want me to do your dirty work for you?'

The Time Lord twirled his umbrella. 'Your sentence will come up for review one day, Doctor. Any service you have rendered the Council will be—considered.'

The Doctor knew he was trapped, but perversely refused to admit it.

'I'm not going to worry about a renegade like the Master. The fellow's an unimaginative plodder.'

The Time Lord chuckled. 'You graduated at the same time, did you not? I believe his degree in Cosmic Science was in a higher category than yours?'

'I was a late developer,' said the Doctor defensively.

'Besides,' the Time Lord went on, 'would you call that little surprise unimaginative?'

He pointed towards the door of the control cabin. The Doctor peered through the crack. At first he saw only a deserted control room. Then he noticed an elaborate arrangement of thin twine leading from the inside handle of the door to a small metal canister perched precariously on the edge of a tall computer cabinet. The Doctor peered at the canister. 'It's a Volataliser,' he said incredulously. 'The Xanthoids use them for mining operations. If that thing falls—'

The Time Lord nodded. 'It will destroy this tower, the Research Centre and about one square mile of the surrounding countryside. You will observe, Doctor, that the door opens outwards. The tension on the twine is such that the slightest touch on the door will cause the cylinder to fall. An amusing idea.'

The Doctor looked at him grimly. 'Then you'd better think up some witty way of dealing with it.'

'I'm sorry, Doctor,' said the Time Lord. He shimmered and vanished, leaving a faint 'good luck' floating on the air.

The Doctor turned back to the door and considered the problem. He could try to untie the twine at the door-handle end. But the door was open the merest crack. He'd never get his fingers through. He could climb on top of the cabin and get through the skylight—but the vibration he would cause might make the cylinder roll off. No, there was only one thing for it.

The Doctor paused for a moment, calculating tension, angle velocities, and the effects of gravity on the estimated weight of the cylinder.

He took a pace back, braced a foot against the guard rail, and gripped the door handle. Then he yanked the door open and catapulted himself head first into the cabin.

3

The Master Takes Over

The Doctor's violent tug on the door was a vital part of his plan. It meant that the twine was drawn taut with a sudden jerk. The metal cylinder didn't just *roll* off the cabinet, it was *snatched* off, travelling about a foot across the cabin towards the door before it started to fall. The Doctor dived headlong across the cabin, hands outstretched, and the cylinder dropped neatly into his outstretched palm. He hit the cabin floor with a thud, but the deadly little cylinder was clutched safely in his hand.

For a moment the Doctor lay there, stretched out at full length. He took a deep shuddering breath. His reflexes were literally super-human, but to stake his life on reaching the falling cylinder in time had been a tremendous gamble, even for him.

Cautiously he sat up. With his free hand, he fished in his pockets, and produced his sonic screwdriver. He turned the cylinder over to reveal a tiny, almost invisible screw in its base. He held the tip of the sonic screwdriver close to it and activated it. There was a faint hum and the little screw began to rotate. Carefully the Doctor began to dismantle the cylinder, extracting the explosive core.

The Brigadier entered the cabin a few minutes later, followed by Jo, Captain Yates, and the Director of the Research Centre. They found the Doctor sitting cross-legged on the floor, a number of oddly shaped pieces of shining metal in his hand.

The Brigadier looked down at him. 'What have you got there, Doctor?'

'A bomb.'

The Brigadier took a hurried step back, bumping into

the Director, who was just behind him. 'Good Lord! Is it safe?'

The Doctor got to his feet and put the assembly of pieces down in the top of a computer cabinet. 'It is now,' he said. He began examining the readings on the rows of instruments in the control cabin.

The Brigadier cleared his throat. 'I've been having a chat with the Director, and I think I've got the picture. He'll tell you what happened.'

The Doctor looked up and gave the Director one of his sudden, charming smiles. 'Let me see if I can guess. Someone switched the radio-telescope beam to a completely different setting, and then boosted the apparatus to full power.'

The Director, a fat and fussy little man, stared at him in amazement. 'That's right. How did you know?'

The Doctor waved a hand at the instruments. 'It's all recorded here. Besides, that's what I expected to happen.'

'Ah, but that isn't all,' said the Director importantly. 'There was also . . .'

The Doctor smiled.

'A sudden surge of power *back* through the telescope?'

'That's right. Several of the circuits were completely burnt out . . .' The Director broke off, looking at the Doctor resentfully. 'There really seems to be very little I can tell you.'

'There never is,' muttered the Brigadier.

'Nonsense, sir,' said the Doctor soothingly. 'You're being a tremendous help. I gather you've also lost a couple of scientists?'

'That's right. Goodge and Phillips. They were the only ones on duty at the time. Devoted to the project, both of them.'

'Fully checked by security, too,' added the Brigadier. 'Impeccable records.'

'Yes, I'm sure,' said the Doctor absently. Lost in thought he wandered around the cabin, hands deep in his pockets. The others watched him. He came to a halt by a table holding a large tin box. 'What's this?'

The Director said, 'That—oh, it's Goodge's lunch box. He lived quite near here. Always brought his own lunch when he was on this shift. Wasn't satisfied with the canteen. Wasn't satisfied with the packed lunch either, I gather.'

The Brigadier looked on irritably as the Doctor tried to open the box.

'Really, Doctor, I hardly think you'll find anything in there.'

The Doctor lifted the lid, peered inside the lunch box and said grimly, 'Won't I? What about one of your missing scientists?'

He held the box towards them, and they all crowded round to see. Jo wriggled to the front of the little group and looked inside the box. On top of some sandwiches and a couple of cold hard-boiled eggs lay some kind of doll, the figure of a little man about six inches long. 'What is it?' she asked. 'A toy?'

The Doctor's voice was grim. 'No. Not a toy.'

Behind her Jo heard the Director gasp as he peered over her shoulder. 'It's impossible . . . but . . . it's Goodge!' he stammered.

Jo looked again. With incredulous horror she saw that the thing in the lunch box was a tiny, shrunken corpse.

*   *   *   *   *

Much later, back at the UNIT laboratory, Jo still hadn't recovered from the shock. 'Doctor, I don't understand. What *happened* to that poor man?'

The Doctor made a squeezing gesture with his hands. 'He was imploded, Jo, the opposite of being exploded.'

Jo shuddered. 'Why would anyone do such a terrible thing?'

'I think it was someone's idea of a joke,' said the Doctor. But there was no amusement in his voice.

'And that booby-trap thing with the twine?'

'Another jolly little prank. *E*xplosion for me, implosion for poor Mr. Goodge. Just the sort of thing to amuse the Master.'

The Brigadier entered just in time to catch this last remark. 'Who the blazes is the Master?'

The Doctor gave them a brief summary of the Master's past exploits and his general character. 'Sort of criminal master-mind, eh?' said the Brigadier shrewdly. 'You're convinced he's working with the Nestenes?'

'Almost certainly. I was warned that he was here—and this business at the Research Centre confirms it.'

'What was the point of it all?' asked Jo. 'Apart from a bit of nasty fun, that is?'

'Don't you see?' said the Doctor patiently. 'He's opened a channel to the Nestenes. That radio telescope was their bridgehead. They used it to channel energy into that surviving Nestene unit.'

'But what will he do with it?' asked Jo.

The Brigadier had worked out the answer to that one for himself. 'Make more Autons—isn't that so, Doctor?'

The Doctor nodded. 'They'll need another source of plastic.'

'Right!' said the Brigadier decisively. 'We'll start running a check on the factories right away. They won't get away with it so easily this time.'

Only too pleased to have a practical problem to deal with, the Brigadier rushed from the room to set up the checking operation. Jo lingered for a moment. The Doctor had wandered over to the window. He was gazing thoughtfully down at the little canal that ran along the back of the UNIT building, his face drawn and worried. 'It'll be all right, Doctor,' said Jo encouragingly. 'Now we know what they're up to, the Brigadier will find them. After all, you've beaten them before.'

'That's just what worries me, Jo. The Nestene mind is far too intelligent not to learn from that defeat. If they're trying again it must be because they've evolved some new weapon, some new technique. And we don't know what it is. All we can do is wait for the attack . . .'

*   *   *   *   *

Rex Farrel looked carefully round his office, checking that everything was as it should be. The room was immaculately tidy, the huge mahogany-topped desk shining and bare of papers. Rex settled himself in the big chair. Somehow he always felt lost in it, swallowed up by its sheer size. As a child, visiting his father in this same office, he had been allowed for a treat to sit in the big chair and swivel it to and fro. He braced himself, sitting up straighter. Things were different now. At last his father had retired, and *he* was the boss.

He leaned forward and spoke into the intercom. 'You can send Colonel Masters in now.'

Rex rose to his feet as his visitor entered. The colonel was a medium-sized man in a beautifully tailored business suit. The only unusual thing about his appearance was a neat pointed beard. It gave him a slightly foreign look. Rex shook hands with him, then waved him to a seat. 'I've been looking forward to meeting you, Colonel.'

The colonel's voice was deep and mellow. 'It's extremely kind of you to see me at such short notice.'

Farrel smiled. 'Your letter mentioned an extremely large initial order, with a steady repeat business. Any businessman would be interested in that.'

'Particularly,' said the colonel gently, 'a businessman who had extended his factory's capacity to deal with new

32

business—which didn't materialise. And who had bought up an enormous stockpile of raw materials, which was now left on his hands.'

Farrel winced, feeling at an immediate disadvantage. It was quite true that, on taking over from his father, his first action had been to order complete automation. He had spent most of the firm's capital on new machinery, disregarding the advice of McDermot, his father's chief engineer. And he *had* bought enormous quantities of raw materials. It wasn't *his* fault that a slump in the plastic market had left him with a factory working at half its capacity, and an enormous pile of useless chemicals. 'I see you've been doing your homework, Colonel,' he said, trying to put a good face on things.

'Don't worry,' said the colonel soothingly. 'Your installation of new machinery is exactly the reason why I chose your factory. I picked your firm very carefully.'

For once the Master was speaking the truth. He had indeed surveyed the plastics industry very thoroughly, and in young Rex Farrel he had found exactly the man he needed. Farrel was weak, and indecisive. He would make an excellent pawn in the Master's game.

Rex attemped a confident laugh. 'Well, I knew the slump would end eventually! Looks as of you're going to prove me right, eh, Colonel?'

'Believe me, Mr. Farrel,' said the Master solemnly, 'the people I represent can never have too much plastic.'

The Master rose to his feet. He rested both hands on Rex's desk, leaning forward to stare deep into his eyes. Rex shrank back timidly. There was something a bit overpowering about this chap. Worse than father . . .

'If we are to work together, Mr. Farrel,' said the Master, 'it is vital that you remember one thing.'

Farrel fought to keep his voice steady. 'Oh yes? And what might that be?'

'You must remember that *I* am the Master. You

will obey me. You will obey me. You will obey me.'

The deep voice boomed and echoed inside Rex's head. The Master's eyes seemed to bore into his brain. Dominated by his father all his life, conditioned to obedience from early childhood, Farrel was an easy victim. 'You are the Master,' he repeated obediently. 'I will obey. I will obey . . .'

*   *   *   *   *

A few days later there was a short council-of-war in the Brigadier's office. It was short because there was little to talk about. They had made no progress whatsoever. There was still no trace of the missing scientist, Phillips. Moreover, the Brigadier's check on the plastics factories had produced no results, much to the Doctor's disgust. 'All those chaps of yours haven't managed to find anything? Really, Brigadier!' The Doctor swung his long legs in the air and rested his feet on the corner of the Brigadier's desk, tilting his chair back at a precarious angle.

Opposite him the Brigadier sat up stiffly, behind a desk piled high with reports.

'Do you realise how big the plastics industry is? How many firms deal in plastics one way or another? We fed all the reports into the computer as they arrived but nothing's showed up.'

'You're quite sure? insisted the Doctor. 'Are *all* the reports in?'

The Brigadier dived into the pile of papers on his desk and found a checklist. 'Yes, I think so,' he said. 'All except the report from X.39.'.

The Doctor sniffed disapprovingly. He didn't think much of the Brigadier's security mumbo-jumbo. 'And who might X.39 be? Or don't you know?'

'Of course I know, Doctor,' said the Brigadier crossly. He scrabbled again in his pile of papers and found a second checklist which he compared with the first.

'Agent X.39 happens to be . . . wait a minute . . . Jo Grant!' The Brigadier looked up triumphantly.

Even in his disgruntled mood, the Doctor managed to raise a smile. 'Oh well, that explains it,' he said. 'I doubt if we'll learn much from her. She's probably lost!'

*　　　*　　　*　　　*　　　*

Jo Grant had had great difficulty in persuading the Brigadier to let her take part in the check at all. At her briefing, he had emphasised that she was to make only a preliminary check. If she discovered anything at all, however trivial, she was to report it at once to her superiors. Jo had nodded obediently, and gone off to start work.

The first few factories she had visited she had stuck strictly to the rules. Everyone had been polite and helpful, answering all her questions quite freely. No one had encountered any big new customers or any demand for bulk supplies of plastics. At the last factory on her list, the young manager had been particularly nice. Yet, as she left his factory, Jo was aware of a tiny, nagging feeling of unease. There was something about Rex Farrel. Perhaps he was too helpful. He had been over-anxious to convince her that everything was normal. Yet sometimes he had seemed to 'shut off' as if in a momentary trance. While she was in the office a secretary had entered with a message from Colonel Masters. Farrel had chased her away. Jo knew quite well that it was her duty to report her suspicions to UNIT. And she knew quite well, too, what would happen. Either they would be ignored, or at best a more senior agent would be sent to make a further check.

Jo decided that modern intelligence methods failed to make proper allowance for women's intuition. She made her way round to the rear of the factory and climbed nimbly over the locked back gate.

She found herself in a bare concrete yard. Piles of chemical drums were stacked everywhere around her. She made her way through them and tried the rear door of the factory. It was locked. But there was a small open window high in the rear wall of the building.

Jo searched through the metal drums till she found one that was empty. She discovered she could shift it quite easily. Quickly she moved it under the window. Looking round she saw a smaller drum, and perched it on top of the big one. She climbed on to the big drum, then stepped up on to the smaller one. The sill of the open window was just within her reach. Jo sprang up, heaved herself on to the sill, and pulled herself through the window. Once through, she perched on the sill for a moment, wriggled herself around, hung by her hands at arms' length, and let herself drop.

Jo scrambled to her feet and ducked for cover behind a bubbling tank of plastic fluid. Cautiously, she peered out from her hiding place.

She was in a long, low, building packed with ultra-modern machinery. There was no one in sight. The machines throbbed and hummed quietly to themselves, as if they needed no help from man. Obviously the whole place was completely automated. Then Jo heard voices, and the sound of footsteps coming towards her.

She slipped between the rows of machines to a point where she could see the two men. One of them was Farrel, the other a dark man with a little beard. As they came nearer she could hear them talking.

'. . . but this will mean a complete alteration of our entire production line,' Farrel was saying.

The other man nodded. 'Exactly.'

Farrel looked worried. 'I don't know what my father . . .'

'Don't worry about your father, Mr. Farrel. You're under a new thumb now.'

'What about that girl from UNIT?' she heard Farrel say.

The second man laughed. 'You dealt with her admirably. I'm rather surprised to hear that they've descended to using children.'

The two men were beginning to move out of earshot, and Jo slipped between the machinery to follow them. But, as she moved, her elbow caught an oil can that had been left on one of the machines. It clattered to the concrete floor, and the two men stopped and swung round. Jo turned to run, but the bearded man's voice rang out commandingly. 'Stop!' The deep voice seemed to freeze her willpower. She found she couldn't move. She turned reluctantly, and immediately became aware of the man's burning gaze fixed upon her. 'Come here!' Jo tried to resist, but those compelling eyes seemed to draw her towards him. 'Follow me.' The Master turned and strode away, and Jo followed obediently after him.

Ten minutes later, she was sitting on a chair in Farrel's office in a deep hypnotic trance. The Master was standing over her, while Farrel looked on worriedly.

'You will return to UNIT with a negative report,' the Master was saying. 'You will tell them that you found nothing suspicious.'

'Nothing suspicious,' Jo repeated in a flat, toneless voice.

'Your instructions concerning the Doctor are already implanted. You will obey them without further word from me. The box has been placed in the boot of your car.'

'I shall obey.'

'Excellent,' said the Master briskly. 'Now then, Miss Grant, at the snap of my fingers you will believe you are concluding your *first* interview with Mr. Farrel. You will remember nothing that happened after that, and you have never seen me.'

The Master snapped his fingers, once, like a pistol shot. Jo came to life and stood up. 'Well, thank you so much for your co-operation, Mr. Farrel,' she said, just as she had done an hour before. Ignoring the Master, she walked towards the door.

Farrel stood up. 'Not at all, a great pleasure. Let me see you out.'

As Farrel showed Jo from the room, the Master chuckled softly to himself. It appealed to his sense of humour to employ the Doctor's assistant as a weapon against him.

*   *   *   *   *

The Doctor peered thoughtfully at the dematerialisation circuit. He cleaned off a little more of the sticky foam left by Jo's efforts with the fire extinguisher. He heard the door open and Jo's voice say 'Hullo, Doctor.'

'Hello, Jo,' he answered, without looking up. 'Back at last are you? Any luck with your plastics factories?'

'Not a thing, Doctor. The Brigadier asked me to bring this up to you. It was found near the Deep Space Research Centre.

The Doctor looked up. Jo was putting an army ammunition box down on the bench. He jumped down from his stool. 'It's the box the Nestene energy unit was in. Probably empty by now. Still, let's take a look.'

The Doctor tried to get the box open. 'Seems to be locked. Funny—if they abandoned it, why lock it?'

Jo said, 'I'll get it open for you.' To the Doctor's amusement she produced a big bunch of keys and started trying to fit one into the lock.

'Here, let me,' said the Doctor. He tried to help her, but she pushed him aside with surprising force.

'*I'll* open it. I *must* open it.'

The Doctor looked at her narrowly. Suddenly he grabbed her by the wrist and moved her away from the box. He put the palm of his other hand on the box. He felt heat, and some kind of vibration.

'Don't open it, Jo! I think it's a bomb!'

Jo broke from the Doctor's grip and returned to the box. The Doctor tried to move her away again but she was amazingly strong. 'I must open it, I must open it,' she muttered obsessively. Despite all the Doctor's efforts she managed to get a key in the lock and twist. Smoke poured from the lock, and the lid of the box began to glow fiercely . . .

4

Death at the Plastics Factory

It took all the Doctor's strength to pull Jo away. She fought him desperately, and although she was unable to escape, her struggles prevented the Doctor from dealing with the box. By now it was glowing white hot, and giving out clouds of choking smoke.

The laboratory door opened and the Brigadier and Captain Yates entered. To their amazement they saw Jo and the Doctor fighting fiercely.

At the sight of them, the Doctor lifted Jo off her feet, and literally threw her across the room. 'Hold her!' he yelled. Jo cannoned into the two soldiers like a well aimed ball in a skittle alley. All three collapsed in a tangle of arms and legs.

The Doctor whipped off his jacket and wrapped it round the box. Immediately the jacket started to burn. The Doctor ran to the window and hurled the blazing bundle through the glass. There was a shattering crash, a splash, then a tremendous 'whumph'. The Doctor saw a tremendous waterspout surge up from the little canal. There were clouds of steam, and the murky water hissed and bubbled.

The dishevelled Brigadier, who had managed to untangle himself from Jo and Yates, came and stood beside the Doctor, looking down at the seething canal. 'There'll be complaints about that, you know,' he said disapprovingly.

The Doctor looked at him with grim amusement. 'My dear Lethbridge-Stewart, if I hadn't got rid of that box, none of us would have been here to listen to them.'

'Suppose you're right,' said the Brigadier philosophically. 'What was that thing?'

'Saturnian solar bomb. Produces intense, localised heat. It would have charred everything and everyone in this room into a heap of fine white ash.'

The Brigadier shuddered. 'How the blazes did it get past the security checks?'

'I'm afraid Jo brought it in.'

'Nonsense. Miss Grant would never . . .'

'Look at her!' interrupted the Doctor. The Brigadier turned. Jo was standing quietly beside Yates, her eyes vacantly staring into space.

'Miss Grant,' snapped the Brigadier. Jo didn't move.

'She can't hear you,' said the Doctor gently. 'She's in a state of post-hypnotic shock.'

'Hypnotised?' repeated the Brigadier incredulously. 'Who did it?'

'The Master, of course. Why else do you think she tried to send us all up in smoke?' The Doctor crossed to Jo, and pushed her gently into a chair. Jo gazed ahead unseeing, as the Doctor peered into her eyes, and took her pulse.

Captain Yates said, 'Look here, Doctor, I thought no hypnotist could make anyone do anything they didn't want to?'

'Not the average hypnotist, perhaps. But the Master can manipulate the human mind as he pleases.'

'Can he take over anyone he likes?' asked the Brigadier

worriedly. He had visions of a platoon of hypnotised secret agents on his hands.

The Doctor continued to examine Jo. 'Not quite. Those with a particularly stubborn nature can resist *any* hypnosis. He'd have quite a job with you, for instance!'

The Brigadier stroked his moustache thoughtfully, trying to work out whether or not this was a compliment. 'In any case,' the Doctor went on, 'even when he's successful the control isn't always permanent. Away from the Master's influence, the human mind struggles constantly to free itself.' He straightened up with a sigh.

'Can you do anything for her?' Yates asked anxiously.

'I'm not sure,' said the Doctor. 'Her mind's been subjected to tremendous strain. I can try, but we mustn't push her too hard.'

He leaned over Jo, tilted her chin up with his hands, and gazed deeply into her eyes. 'Jo . . . Josephine Grant! Listen to me . . . this is the Doctor. Can you hear me?'

For a moment there was no reply, then Jo said faintly, 'The box . . . I *had* to open it . . .'

Reassuringly, the Doctor said, 'That's all over now. Who gave you the box? Who told you to open it? Was it the Master?'

An expression of fear crossed Jo's face. 'The Master. I must obey the Master.'

'Where is he, Jo? Where did you see him?'

Jo became rigid with terror. Her eyes widened, and she whispered, 'The Master . . . I must obey . . . I must obey . . .'

The Doctor snapped, 'Jo—listen to me!' She fell silent. 'You will sleep now, you will forget everything that has happened. You will forget your meeting with the Master. *You will forget any orders that he has given you.* Sleep . . . you will sleep now.'

Jo's head nodded onto her chest, and Yates had to catch her to stop her slipping off her chair. 'Better get

41

her to sick bay,' said the Doctor. 'She should be all right when she wakes up.'

Gently Yates lifted Jo up in his arms and carried her out of the laboratory.

The Doctor turned to the Brigadier and said, 'That's the best I can do, I'm afraid. I've returned her to normal and erased all the Master's commands. If I press her for information, her mind might very well snap.'

The Brigadier sighed. 'So we're no better off, then?'

'Oh, I wouldn't say that. We know we're on the right lines. Presumably Jo met the Master at one of those factories she visited. How many were on her list?'

'Nine,' said the Brigadier gloomily. 'But surely it must have all happened at the last one she visited?'

The Doctor shook his head. 'Not necessarily. The Master would have given her a post-hypnotic command. If she'd met him at the first factory on her list, she'd still have gone on and visited all the rest.'

'We'll re-check the lot of them,' said the Brigadier decisively.

The Doctor held up a warning finger. 'But discreetly, please. We want to know where the Master is, but we don't want to scare him off.'

'Right you are,' said the Brigadier. He paused at the door. 'Doctor—what about that machine you used against the Autons last time? If we were to get that mass-produced . . .'

'What would be the point? You have to get within inches of them to use it. It worked before because they weren't expecting it. This time they'll be prepared. They may even have evolved a defence . . .'

The Brigadier's face fell. 'Then how *are* we going to deal with them?'

The Doctor turned and looked through the shattered window. Quietly he said, 'I haven't the faintest idea.'

*   *   *   *   *

In the Research Laboratory of the plastic factory, the Master had moved in some very special machinery. Transparent pipes from the main supply reservoir fed into a coffin-shaped tank of plastic mix, which bubbled and seethed. Also connected to the tank was a complicated control panel.

On a table nearby rested the Nestene energy unit, pulsing with a livid green light. In the Master's hand was the linking device he had used at the radio telescope. Carefully he attached one set of terminals to the globe, the other to the bubbling tank. The energy unit began to pulse with increased power. The Master looked intently down into the tank of liquid plastic. Slowly a shape began to form. First a body, then arms and legs, finally the face, blank, lumpy, unfinished, a terrifying parody of humanity. Liquid plastic streaming from its head and shoulders, the giant figure sat upright, then clambered stiffly out of the tank. At a gesture from the master it moved across the room and stood motionless against the wall.

The Master adjusted controls, and a fresh supply of plastic mix began to flow into the tank. There was a timid tap on the door. The Master opened it and Rex entered. The newly-born Auton raised its arm to strike, and Rex cowered back.

The Master snapped, 'No!' The Auton lowered its arm and stood motionless once more. Farrel stood quite still, petrified with fear. 'I told you never to come here,' said the Master.

Farrel edged away from the Auton. 'It's McDermot—he's come back!'

'And who is McDermot?' asked the Master patiently.

'He's my production manager. He started the firm with father. He's been away on a trip. He wants to know what's been going on. He's making trouble, threatening to tell my father.' Rex was almost babbling in his panic.

Slowly a shape began to form . . .

The Master considered for a moment. 'Then we shall have to deal with him.' The coffin-shaped tank was full again. The Master moved across to the controls console and turned a valve to cut off the flow. He gazed thoughtfully into the bubbling plastic for a moment, then gave a sudden chilling laugh. 'We'll demonstrate one of our new products, shall we?'

The Master leaned over the controls and made rapid readjustments, his fingers flickering across the keyboard. Inside the coffin-shaped tank another shape was forming. The Master watched it, smiling to himself. Such a versatile material, plastic . . .

*   *   *   *   *

McDermot, a tough, stocky Northcountryman in his fifties, was on the phone in Rex Farrel's office. A brief tour of the factory had convinced him that Rex's father should be informed at once. He was talking to him now in a low, urgent voice. 'It's true I tell you . . . aye, that's right. All the staff's been dismissed. Regular customers told we can't supply them. New machinery brought in, a secret research lab. I'm sorry, Mr. Farrel, but I think young Rex has gone right round the bend. Keeps on about this fellow, Colonel Masters. Right, sir, I'll tell them to hold everything, and that you're on your way. I'll wait for you here.'

Rex entered with the Master who was carrying a black plastic bundle.

McDermot slammed down the phone and swung round angrily. 'You'll be Rex's precious Colonel Masters, I take it? Just the man I wanted to see!'

The Master smiled. 'You *are* seeing me, Mr. McDermot.' The angry engineer wasn't listening. 'Just what right do you think you've got to come marching in here and ruin a decent little family business? Me and Rex's dad built this place up from nothing. I'll not stand by and

45

see it all thrown away by a daft kid and some foreign jackanapes with big ideas.'

The Master's eyes blazed with sudden anger, but he kept his voice quiet and pleasant. 'You're being less than fair, Mr. McDermot. The new processes and products I have introduced are truly revolutionary.' The Master held out the bundle of plastic sheeting over his arm.

McDermot snatched it from him and snorted in disgust. 'That—revolutionary? It's the wrong colour, the wrong texture. It's got a cold, clammy feel . . .'

He threw the plastic bundle back at the Master in disgust.

The Master caught it. 'I assure you, you don't realise its full potential . . . Allow me to demonstrate.' He threw the bundle of plastic into a corner, then snapped his fingers. The plastic sheeting began to move and swell, as if alive. McDermot looked on, shaken, as the plastic writhed and grew. Slowly but surely it was taking on the shape of a chair. A squashy, bulgy, black armchair, made of plastic. McDermot snorted. 'You think you'll sell *that*? It's one of the ugliest things I've seen in my life.'

'It's very comfortable,' said the Master smoothly. 'Try it.'

Somehow McDermot didn't fancy the idea. There was something very sinister about that squat black shape. 'No thanks,' he said, backing away.

With a sudden fierce authority the Master snapped, 'Sit down, man!'

Without quite knowing why, McDermot lowered himself uneasily into the chair. Its arms felt cold and slithery to the touch. 'Disgusting stuff, this,' he muttered. 'What do you call it?'

The Master smiled coldly. 'Polynestene!' he said, and began to laugh. The armchair billowed and surged, and McDermot felt himself sinking lower and lower. He struggled to get up but the plastic seemed to cling to him.

His arms and legs were trapped. A tide of cold clammy black plastic rose over his head and swallowed him up, choking off his attempt to scream . . . The last thing McDermot heard was the Master's mocking laughter.

Rex looked on appalled as the heaving black shape in the corner swallowed McDermot, completely. He made an instinctive move as if to help the doomed engineer, but the Master held him back. 'No! I will not tolerate the insolence of primitives.'

The Master snapped his fingers. An Auton appeared in the doorway, gathered up the shapeless black bundle and carried it from the room.

Regretfully, the Master watched the armchair disappear. 'An amusing little conceit—but rather laborious!'

White and shaking, Rex sank into his chair. 'It seemed very effective,' he said.

The Master smiled. 'But so extravagant, my dear Rex. All very well for my little joke—but for the mass attack, we have better means. Why use yards and yards of precious plastic for a task that can be accomplished by a mere few inches?'

Rex stared at him uncomprehendingly. 'Inches?'

'The human body has one central weakness,' said the Master savagely. 'One which I shall exploit to bring about the destruction of mankind.'

5

The Killer Doll

Jo Grant stopped and braced herself, before entering the Doctor's laboratory. It's difficult to know what to say to someone you've tried to blow up—even if you were under the influence of hypnosis at the time.

As she came in, a UNIT technician was putting the final touches to his repair of the Doctor's window. Jo had no recollection of what had happened at the laboratory the previous day, but she had made Captain Yates tell her the full story. She felt a sudden wave of guilt, and her murmured apology dried up in her throat.

The technician packed up his tools and went on his way. The Doctor turned to Jo, with a smile of pleasure. He reached out and took her by the shoulders. 'Are you sure you're all right, Jo? You really shouldn't be up, you know!'

The welcome was obviously genuine, and Jo felt like crying with relief. 'Oh Doctor, I'm so sorry,' she stammered.

The Doctor looked baffled. 'Sorry? What ever for?'

'That box—I might have killed you!'

'Oh I see,' said the Doctor. 'My dear girl, you mustn't worry about that. That wasn't you—it was the Master.' His matter of fact tone made it clear that this took care of the matter. There was no more to be said.

When the Brigadier came in he saw to his horror that Jo was blinking away tears. He covered his embarrassment with military formality. 'Miss Grant, you're supposed to be on sick leave.'

Jo gave him a tearful smile. 'I'm all right now, honestly.'

'You haven't *remembered* by any chance?' the Brigadier said hopefully.

Jo shook her head. 'I keep trying and trying, but nothing comes.'

'Then *don't* try,' said the Doctor. 'Leave your mind alone and something will probably pop up.'

'That's as maybe, Doctor,' said the Brigadier irritably. 'But we are scarcely in a position to wait for something to "pop up" from Miss Grant's subconscious.'

'What about those agents of yours?'

48

'Nothing but negative reports so far. I've a good mind to surround and search every factory on that list.'

The Doctor took a deep breath. 'Your methods, my dear Lethbridge-Stewart, have all the refined subtlety of a bull in a china shop . . .'

What looked like quite a promising quarrel was broken up by the entrance of Captain Yates. He was somewhat embarrassed to find his two superiors glaring at each other, eyeball to eyeball. He cleared his throat and they both turned to him. 'Well?' snapped the Brigadier. 'Don't stand there coughing at me.'

'Message from one of the field sections,' said Yates hurriedly. 'A bit tenuous but I thought I'd . . .'

'Out with it, man,' the Brigadier barked.

'You remember Professor Phillips—the chap who disappeared from the Deep Space Research Station? His car disappeared with him, and the police have just spotted it.'

The Doctor looked hopeful. 'Now that's more like it. Where?'

'That's the funny thing, Doctor. Parked amongst a lot of circus vehicles in a field at a place called Tarminster.'

The Doctor gave a sudden grin. All his bad temper was gone, and he looked like a schoolboy off on a treat. 'You know,' he said, 'it's years and years since I've been to a circus!'

The Brigadier said thoughtfully, 'I've got every available man checking those plastics factories. I'll have to recall some of them to check this circus.'

'Don't do that,' said the Doctor. 'Their work's too important. I'll take care of this myself—after all, it may not come to anything. Got any photographs of Phillips?'

The Brigadier was a bit bewildered by the Doctor's burst of energy. 'Some in my office, I think.'

'Let's have 'em then.' The Doctor was already on his way out of the door.

The Brigadier followed him. 'Now see here, Doctor,'

he protested. 'I still think you ought to leave this sort of thing to my chaps . . .'

'Nonsense—I'll make a much better job of it . . .'

The sound of their heated voices disappeared down the corridor. Yates couldn't help grinning, but there was no answering smile from Jo.

Yates looked at Jo sympathetically. 'What's the matter, then?'

'Oh nothing!' Jo said bitterly. 'Life's just marvellous.'

'Easy, love,' he said soothingly.

Once she'd started, Jo couldn't stop herself. 'I've made a really terrific start here, haven't I? I find the man everyone's looking for, forget where he is, and finish up trying to kill the Doctor.'

'No one's blaming you,' said Yates. This just made Jo more angry.

'Oh no, no one blames me. They just say go and lie down and don't bother us. I'm not a child, you know.'

'No? Then you'd better stop acting like one.'

Jo glared at Yates angrily, and then realised he was quite right.

'Sorry. Didn't mean to to take it out on you. But if only there was some way I could show them . . .'

'Don't try,' advised Yates. 'Do as the Brigadier said—go back to bed.'

Jo nodded, and turned to leave. Then she paused. 'Where did you say that car was found?'

'In a circus near Tarminster—why?'

'Oh nothing,' said Jo. 'Just curious, that's all.' She hurried off down the corridor.

*   *   *   *   *

Rex Farrel sat behind his big desk, head buried in his hands. He couldn't work out why he was so worried. Everything was going well. The Master had said so, and the Master was always right. UNIT had paid a second visit to the factory—a polite young man this time, obviously a soldier for all his civilian clothing. He had inspected the factory, looking at the new automated machinery uncomprehendingly. Rex had showed him the faked production records prepared by the Master, and he had gone away apparently satisfied. Yet, in spite of all this, there was a terrible feeling on Rex's mind that things *weren't* all right. Somehow they were terribly wrong. McDermot, for instance. Something had happened to McDermot. If only he could remember . . . His mind seemed to shy away from the thought. All he could hear was the voice of the Master, telling him he must obey.

'Rex! What the devil's the matter with you?'

The sound of an all-too-familiar voice jolted Rex from his reverie. His father was standing in the doorway. Rex felt the beginning of that familiar helplessness that crept over him whenever his father was angry.

John Farrel looked down at his son with concern. Farrel Senior was a big, tough, self-made man, who had bullied his way to the top through sheer determination. Even in his sixties, he was an imposing figure. Unable to accept that Rex hadn't inherited his own strength, he had always treated him harshly in an attempt to 'put some spine into the boy.' As a natural result, Rex had grown up feeble and indecisive, always living in his father's shadow.

It had been Rex's mother who had talked her husband into retiring and letting Rex take over the factory. She realised that the boy would never really grow up until he could get away on his own. John Farrel had been persuaded against his will. He was not surprised to hear from McDermot that things were already in an unholy mess. But he loved his son, in his own way, and was genuinely distressed to see the boy looking so desperately haggard. 'Rex,' he said again, 'what's the matter? What's been going on here? Are you ill?'

'No, no, I'm fine. Never been better. What brings you here?'

'McDermot phoned me. Where is he?'

Rex looked confused. 'He's not here. He went away.'

'Away? He said he'd meet me *here*! Where did he go?'

'I don't know,' Rex stammered. 'I think it was a business trip . . .'

By now, John Farrel was convinced that something was very wrong indeed. McDermot missing, Rex dithering like an idiot . . . And the boy looked terrible. He was obviously on the point of a nervous breakdown. Farrel jumped as a deep voice spoke behind him. 'Mr. Farrel senior, I take it?'

A dark, foreign-looking man with a pointed beard had entered the office. He smiled politely. 'Allow me to introduce myself. I am Colonel Masters.'

Rex chimed in, his voice eager and deferential. 'The colonel has placed a tremendous order, father. He's going to take up our entire output.'

'Not if I have any say in the matter,' said John Farrel grimly.

Rex babbled on. 'We're changing our entire policy, father. Introducing new methods, new products . . .'

Farrel shouted, 'You're doing nothing of the kind, Rex. You'll continue to operate this factory on the lines I laid down, or I'll dismiss you and do the job myself. I'm still the major shareholder, you know.'

'Mr. Farrel!' The authority in Colonel Masters' voice made John Farrel jump. He opened his mouth to argue, but the colonel was advancing on him menacingly, dark eyes blazing with some inner light. 'Listen to me, Mr. Farrel,' said the deep, hypnotic voice. 'The changes I have suggested are for the good of your factory. They *must* be carried through. You must believe me. You must believe me. There is nothing to worry about.'

'Nothing to worry about.' repeated Farrel obediently.

For a moment Farrel felt his mind coming under the spell of that compelling personality. With tremendous effort he broke free. 'I do *not* believe you,' he growled, 'and there is a great deal to worry about. Frankly, your presence here worries me more than anything else.'

He saw the Colonel's face distort with rage. He thought that the man was actually going to strike him. Then Rex leaped between them. 'No,' he shouted. 'No, you mustn't.'

The Colonel lowered his arm, and forced a smile. 'Congratulations, Mr. Farrel. I can usually overcome opposition. Your will is very strong. In fact, dangerously so !'

The Colonel stalked out of the room, and Farrel was glad to see him go. Feeling strangely shaken, he turned to his son. 'Rex, hadn't you better go home ? I'll deal with things here.'

The words roused Rex to a frenzy. 'No, father, don't say that. Leave it all to me, please.'

Farrel looked at him. Then he said reluctantly, 'All right, I'll give you till tomorrow, Rex. By then I want that Masters fellow out of here, and the factory on the way back to normal. If not, I'll dismiss you and take over.'

Rex spoke in a dull voice, without looking up. 'Very well, father. I'll do as you say.'

Farrel was still uncertain, but he felt sure Rex would obey him. After all, he always had. 'Well,' he said gruffly. 'Better be on my way. Try and take better care of yourself.'

Minutes later Farrel was striding angrily towards his Bentley. He'd parked in his old slot in the company car park. He unlocked the car and was getting behind the wheel when he heard someone call his name. 'Mr. Farrel —won't you wait a moment ?'

Farrel looked up, and saw the Colonel hurrying towards him, a large cardboard box under his arm. Farrel got in the car and started the engine. As the Colonel came up to him, he wound down the window and said, 'Well?'

There was no trace of anger now in the Colonel's manner. He was all smoothness and charm. 'I thought I might make a last attempt to win you over. Let me show you one of our new lines.' He opened the box and held it out.

Farrel recoiled in horror. Inside the box was one of the most evil-looking dolls he had ever seen in his life. A squat, hairy thing, with a slant-eyed oriental face, and a straggly tuft of beard. Enough to scare any child into fits. Unconsciously, he echoed the words of McDermot. 'It's the ugliest thing I've ever seen in my life.'

'Not for children, of course,' said the Colonel. 'A novelty, for the adult market.'

'Keep it,' snapped Farrel. 'I don't want the thing!' He switched on the ignition.

'But I insist,' said the Master. With a sudden quick movement, he thrust the box through the car window, tossing it on the back seat.

For a moment Farrel was tempted to throw it out again, but he decided it would be simpler to ignore it. He put the car into gear, and accelerated away so quickly that Colonel Masters had to jump out of the way.

As the Bentley swept out of the car park and disappeared down the road the Master stood looking after it. He stroked his beard and smiled. 'Simply testing out a new product, Mr. Farrel,' he said gently. 'I do hope you enjoy the demonstration.'

John Farrel had a long drive in front of him. Aware of his anger, he realised he was driving too fast, and forced himself to slow down to a sensible pace. In his hurry to get away, he hadn't noticed that the heater was turned on full. The temperature in the car began to rise.

Although he was driving with automatic care, Farrel's

54

mind was still full of events at the factory. He was a tough, unimpressionable man, but something about the Master had frightened him badly. If the fellow wasn't gone by tomorrow, he'd put the police on to him, he decided.

Behind him, on the back seat, the lid of the cardboard box began to move. Slowly it was pushed off, as the little doll inside sat up. It looked round, its slanting eyes shining evilly, then fixed its gaze on the back of Farrel's neck. Slowly it leaned forward, clambered jerkily onto all fours, and crouched cat-like as if ready to spring ...

At the wheel Farrel became aware that he was much too hot. He switched off the heater, and rolled the front window right down. A blast of cold air swept through the car. The little doll toppled over and lay motionless.

Later that afternoon Farrel turned into the driveway of his country house. He garaged the car and got out. As he was locking it, he noticed that the doll was out of its box, lying sprawled across the back seat. He frowned for a moment, stuffed it back in the box, and carried it into the house.

*　　　*　　　*　　　*　　　*

The Doctor was having a wonderful time. He strolled round the circus field, looking at the busy scene with child-like enjoyment. The afternoon show was just finishing and he could hear the sounds of music and applause coming from the big top.

The tents and booths of a little fair were clustered around the main tent. Children were running around and about, trying their luck on darts and hoop-la, persuading parents into buying vast quantities of hot dogs, candy-floss, and fizzy lemonade. To the Doctor's delight, there was even an old-fashioned roundabout, with the traditional steam horses. He treated himself to a ride, revolving solemnly round with his fellow passengers, most of whom assumed from his clothes that he was part of the circus.

When the ride was over, the Doctor remembered, rather guiltily, that he was supposed to be here on business. He climbed down from his wooden horse, gave it an affectionate pat on the nose, and made his way round to the back of the big top. He picked his way through the caravans and the animal cages. By the back entrance of the tent, he could see a couple of clowns having a quick smoke while they waited to go on.

A surly looking roustabout came by carrying a bucket of water. The Doctor stopped him. 'Excuse me, old chap, I'm trying to trace a friend of mine. Here's a picture of him. Have you seen him about at all?' Barely looking at the photograph, the man shook his head and disappeared inside a trailer. The Doctor shrugged, and walked up to the clowns. But before he could even show them the photograph of Professor Phillips, they turned and ran back into the tent.

The Doctor tried a lion-tamer, a strong man, and an acrobat—always with the same result. Most of them would barely talk to him, and no one seemed to have seen Phillips.

The Doctor felt puzzled and uneasy. There was something badly wrong here. He'd spent quite a lot of time with circus folk in the past, and always found them hospitable and friendly. He made his way back to the little fair. Perhaps he'd have better luck with some of the stall-holders.

As the Doctor moved away from the big top, a melancholy, white-faced clown watched from behind a trailer. As the Doctor's tall figure disappeared into the crowd, the clown walked swiftly over to a horse-box which was parked in a corner of the field. Even if the Doctor had seen him, he would have found it difficult to recognise the missing Professor Phillips under his garish clown's make-up.

A few moments later, the Master, sitting in Rex's office, was looking into the screen of what looked like a portable television set. The painted face of Professor Phillips looked out at him. 'You're sure it's the Doctor?' enquired the Master.

Phillips' voice was dull and toneless. 'I am sure, Master.'

'Excellent! You know what you must do?'

'Yes, Master. I shall obey.'

The Master touched a switch, and the screen went black. The Master turned to Farrel, who had been looking uncomprehendingly over his shoulder. He was unable to resist boasting, even to such a pitiful audience.

'You see? My plan is working!'

Rex struggled to understand. 'But I thought you had already destroyed the Doctor? The box you sent with the girl . . .'

The Master smiled. 'The bomb was merely a greetings card—a small gallantry on the eve of battle. I wished the Doctor to see my power. To *know* that I have defeated him, before he dies!' In fact, having twice failed to kill the Doctor, the Master was salving his enormous vanity by pretending he'd planned things that way all along. 'Professor Phillips' car has lured the Doctor to the circus —that is the first stage of my plan. Now that he is here, I shall destroy him!'

*   *   *   *   *

John Farrel was telling his wife all about his visit to the factory, with particular emphasis on the way in which he had 'dealt with' the Master.

'He soon changed his tune all right, after I'd told him a thing or two,' said Farrel with satisfaction. 'Started trying to butter me up, even insisted I take this wretched thing.'

His wife shuddered as she looked at the little doll. 'It's a horrible looking thing. There's something evil about it.'

Farrel grunted. 'Well, if he thinks he's turning my factory over to making those things, he can think again.'

'I'm sure you'll deal with things, dear,' said Mary Farrel soothingly. Thirty years of marriage to her forceful husband had convinced her that he was always right, and that he could cope with anyone. Since John Farrel held both these opinions himself, they got on remarkably well. The tragedy was that neither of them had ever encountered anyone as evil and ruthless as the Master.

'I'll make some tea, shall I?' she went on. 'It's getting late.'

Farrel grunted assent, and picked up his paper. Mary Farrel popped the devil doll back in its box, and tossed it on a shelf behind Farrel's armchair. The shelf ran along the wall, just over a central heating radiator.

For a moment the comfortably furnished sitting room was silent. There was only the occasional rustle of Farrel's newspaper, and the sound of Mary Farrel clinking cups in the kitchen. The cardboard box with the doll inside lay forgotten on the shelf.

There came a scrabbling sound. The lid of the box began to move. It was pushed off, from the inside. The little doll sat up. It looked round, its little eyes glinting evilly as they fastened on the back of Farrel's neck. It started to climb out of the box. But the box was near the edge of the shelf. Box and doll overbalanced and fell to the ground.

Farrel jumped at the sound. He looked behind him and saw the doll lying by the skirting board, the box half on top of it. Farrel gave a little grunt of relief and reproved himself for his own jumpiness. Mary must have perched the thing on the edge of the shelf. Somehow it had slipped off. He made a half-movement to pick the doll up, but decided he was too tired to bother. Let the

The doll sprang for his throat

wretched thing stay on the floor. He'd throw it away later.

He turned his attention back to his paper. Slowly and stealthily the doll began to slide from under the box.

Farrel heard a soft 'thump' as something landed on the back of his armchair. He turned his head, and saw that the devil doll was perched on the back of his chair. He gasped in horror. Before he could move, the doll sprang for his throat, clinging with its tiny claw-like hands to his collar. Farrel tried to tear it away, but it clung on with amazing strength. It seemed to *hiss* at him. Suddenly, he found he couldn't breathe . . .

Mary Farrel heard the crash from the kitchen. She ran in at once to find her husband sprawled awkwardly over his armchair, which had fallen over backwards.

She had a fleeting impression of something scuttling away from his throat . . .

6

In the Hands of the Autons

Once she arrived at the Tarminster fair, it didn't take Jo Grant long to spot the Doctor. He was moving from stall to stall, showing the proprietors a photograph of Professor Phillips. Jo hung about for a while, wondering how to approach him. She didn't want to spoil his detective work, and she wasn't too sure how the Doctor was going to react to her presence.

As she followed the Doctor through the crowd she became aware that someone else was following him. Wherever the Doctor went, a melancholy white-faced clown was not far behind. There was something very familiar about that clown. Jo stared hard at him, and suddenly realised what it was. Underneath the clown's make-up was the missing Professor Phillips! The Doctor was being followed by the man he had come to find.

Jo felt she ought to warn the Doctor. But if she went up to him now, Phillips would certainly see her. He might take fright and disappear into the crowd. Jo was still very aware of having 'lost' the Master. She didn't want to make matters worse by losing Professor Phillips too.

The Doctor meanwhile was going on with his search, completely unaware that he was being trailed by both friend and foe. He covered every single stall in the fair. Dodgems, hoop-la, candy floss, coco-nut shy, and many more—they all met his polite enquiries with a surly denial. People at Circus Rossini were not prepared to discuss missing scientists, or anything else. The Doctor wondered again what was wrong. Several of those he had spoken to seemed actually frightened . . . He leaned against a trailer and rubbed his chin, trying to apply logic to the problem.

If Professor Phillips was hiding in the circus, perhaps the Master was too. The Doctor knew that the Master's TARDIS, unlike his own, still had its chameleon mechanism in working order.

This gave it the ability to change appearance, so that wherever it landed it could blend into the landscape. The Doctor's TARDIS had once had this power but, unfortunately, on one of his visits to twentieth century London, the chameleon circuits had worn out, and he had been unable to replace them. Since then, the TARDIS had materialised on many an alien planet in the sturdy, blue shape of a London police box.

Thoughtfully, the Doctor surveyed the circus lorries and trailers parked in the far corner of the site. He spotted what he was looking for almost at once. Standing a little apart from this shabby collection of vehicles was an elegant gleaming, brand-new horse-box. It stood out like a Rolls Royce in a junk-yard. The Doctor nodded in satisfaction, and strolled casually over to it.

He walked all around it, first one way, and then the other. He tried the doors—they were locked. He placed his hand flat against the glossy side, and felt the tingling vibration.

The Doctor smiled to himself. 'Typical,' he thought. 'Had to have the biggest and best horse-box in the place. If he'd materialised it as something shabby, I'd have taken much longer to find him!'

The Doctor returned to the locked doors at the rear of the horse-box. He knew now that no ordinary lock held them closed. But even a TARDIS lock can be picked —if you have the right instruments. The Doctor produced his sonic screwdriver, and bent over the lock.

Absorbed in his task, he didn't hear the sound of rushing footsteps until it was too late. He swung round and was immediately overwhelmed by a little group of brawny roustabouts, the tough labourers who put up the fair and the big top.

The Doctor struggled furiously. A Venusian Aikido throw sent one of his assailants spinning through the air. A jab to a nerve-centre dropped another. Then someone swung a mallet. The Doctor dodged, but the mallet caught him a glancing blow behind the ear, with enough force to send him to his knees. Immediately, the roustabouts grabbed him and dragged him away from the horse-box and into a large ornate caravan, parked nearby.

Watching from her hiding place behind a smaller caravan, Jo Grant had seen the Doctor's examination of the horse-box, and his attempt to pick the lock. Then, before she could shout a warning the little group of men led by the clown had dashed from behind the trailers, overwhelmed the Doctor, and dragged him into the big caravan. For a moment she hovered indecisively. She remembered seeing a call-box in the lane just outside the field. Desperately she began to run towards it. A few minutes later she was inside, putting through a priority call on the UNIT communications circuit.

She poured out her story to the Brigadier. He didn't waste time reproving her—Jo guessed that would come later. 'You are to do nothing at all, Miss Grant. Stay exactly where you are. Help is on the way!'

When the Doctor's head cleared, he found himself inside a very large and ornate caravan. He struggled to rise from his chair, and gave up the idea when he realised that he was tied to it by coil upon coil of rope. A bulging muscled strong man in a leopardskin was winding round the last few coils. Another man dressed as a circus ringmaster stood watching, smoking a big cigar.

The Doctor smiled politely and said, 'Mr. Rossini, of Circus Rossini, I take it?'

The man nodded. 'That's right. And who might you be?'

'You can call me the Doctor. I'll thank you to untie me at once.'

Rossini chuckled and took a puff at his cigar, deliberately blowing smoke into the Doctor's face. 'First you tell me why you're so interested in my friend's horse-box.'

'What's your friend's name?' rapped the Doctor.

Rossini started to answer automatically, obeying the note of authority in the voice. 'His name is—' Then he checked himself, realising that he didn't know the answer. 'That's none of your business.'

'Where does he come from? How long has that horse-box been parked in your field?'

With sudden rage Rossini realised that the prisoner had taken charge of the interrogation.

'You better shut up,' he yelled furiously. 'I ask the questions.'

The Doctor looked at him in quiet amusement, but said nothing. Rossini became even more angry. He nodded to the strong man. 'Tony, see if you can loosen our guest's tongue.'

Somehow hampered by the coils of rope, Tony grabbed the Doctor's bound wrist and attemped to twist it. Rossini grinned nastily. 'You better talk, Mister, or Tony will snap your arm like a carrot!'

Tony, however, was finding things unexpectedly difficult. Twisting the Doctor's wrist was like trying to twist a steel hawser. It simply didn't budge.

The Doctor was keeping his wrist-muscles locked—a trick he had learned from an old Indian Fakir during the Mutiny. But he knew he couldn't keep it up forever against Tony's tremendous strength. Keeping his voice calm and cheerful, he said, 'No need for that. I'm perfectly willing to talk.'

Rossini nodded, and a somewhat puzzled Tony released his grip on the Doctor's wrist, and stepped back. 'Well?' snarled Rossini.

'I'm awfully sorry,' said the Doctor politely. 'I seem to have forgotten the original question.'

Rossini controlled himself with difficulty. 'What were you doing at my friend's horse-box?'

'Trying to get in,' said the Doctor simply. 'You see, I'd detected certain rather interesting vibrations.'

Rossini grunted. 'I don't think my friend is going to like you.'

'I'm afraid you're right,' agreed the Doctor. Then, once again, he rapped out a sudden question. 'By the way, where *is* your friend?'

'Away,' said Rossini quickly. 'Away on business. Now let's find out a little more about *you.*'

Rossini reached inside the Doctor's pocket, and found the photograph of Phillips. It was obvious from his reaction that he recognised it.

'Listen to me,' said the Doctor urgently. 'That is a photograph of a missing Government scientist. If you've had anything to do with concealing him, you're going to find yourself in very serious trouble. You won't find a prison cell as comfortable as this caravan.'

Rossini felt suddenly frightened. He wanted to get away from this tall, stern man, who could coolly issue threats and warnings while lashed to a chair. 'I think we wait and let my friend deal with you.'

'What do you think he'll suggest?' asked the Doctor interestedly.

'The cost of meat is terribly high, Doctor. Maybe my friend lets me feed you to the tigers.'

His confidence a little restored by this rather indifferent joke, Rossini said, 'Watch him, Tony. I got things to do,' and hurriedly left the caravan.

From her hiding place, Jo Grant saw him come down the steps. Scowling to himself, he crossed the field, and disappeared inside the Big Top.

Jo turned and looked down the road. No UNIT jeep was in sight. She thought for a moment. The group of men had dragged the Doctor into the caravan ... The clown had left them and gone into the horse-box ... Rossini and the strong man had entered. The original group of thugs had left, dispersing amongst the trailers. Now Rossini had left. Jo added up all these comings and goings and concluded that only the strong man was left to guard the Doctor.

Her stock of patience and caution, never in very good supply, had been almost used up by her call to the Brigadier and the subsequent wait. She looked down the road again. Still no UNIT jeep. Surely she could deal with just *one* guard. Even if he *was* a strong man ... Cautiously, Jo began to make her way towards the caravan.

The Doctor meanwhile was trying to chat with Tony,

but was finding it heavy going. The strong man refused to say a single word, and the Doctor was beginning to wonder if the man *could* talk. 'You really are the strong and silent type, aren't you,' said the Doctor. He continued his struggle to work free of his bonds, using a technique of muscular contraction learned from his old friend, Houdini.

As he worked, the Doctor glanced idly through the caravan window, and was astonished to see a familiar face peering in at him. It was Jo Grant. The Doctor jerked his head warningly and the face disappeared. Moments later he saw Jo peering through the doorway of the caravan which had been left ajar.

Time for a diversion, he decided. Glaring indignantly at the strong man, he said, 'You've no right to keep me here, you know. I've a good mind to call for help.' And throwing his head back, the Doctor yelled, 'Help!' at the top of his voice.

The strong man jumped to his feet, produced a particularly grubby handkerchief and tried to stuff it in the Doctor's mouth. Meanwhile, Jo Grant slipped into the caravan, jumped on a bunk, and crowned the strong man over the head with an ornate flower pot that was Rossini's pride and joy. Tony crashed to the ground. The Doctor said, 'Jo, what are you doing here? You're supposed to be resting at UNIT H.Q.'

'Just as well for you I'm not, isn't it?' said Jo cheekily. She started undoing the ropes. 'Doctor, I've seen Professor Phillips. He was following you round the fair. When they got you, he went in to one of the horse-boxes.'

'And I bet I know which one,' said the Doctor grimly, as he struggled free.

'What's he doing in a horse-box? Is there a horse inside?'

The Doctor grinned. 'No! No more than there's a policeman inside my police box.'

Inside the Master's horse-box there was, in fact, a huge and glittering control room—huge because the Master's TARDIS, like the Doctor's, was dimensionally transcendental—bigger on the inside than on the outside. Phillips was crouched over a battery of monitor screens. One showed the Doctor and Jo walking across the fairground. Another showed the Master sitting behind Farrel's desk at the plastics factory. His face was dark with anger. 'Since they have escaped, Phillips, *you* must destroy them.'

'I shall obey, Master.'

'Listen carefully. In a locker just beside you is a small egg-shaped sphere, with a contact button inset into the top. Here is what you must do . . .'

Jo and the Doctor were arguing in low tones as they walked towards the Master's horse-box. 'What are we going to *do*, Doctor?' asked Jo. 'Why don't we just get away while we can?'

'I've got to get inside it, Jo. This is a wonderful opportunity, we mustn't waste it.'

They both stopped talking as the rear doors of the horse-box opened. Still wearing his clown costume, Professor Phillips came down the steps and started walking towards them. His eyes were blank and glassy, and there was an egg-shaped silvery sphere in his right hand. He raised the hand above his head in a throwing gesture.

The Doctor put every ounce of authority and power he could into his voice. 'Professor Phillips! Don't!'

He had seen at once that Phillips was carrying a Sontaran fragmentation grenade—one of the most deadly combat weapons in the universe, produced by a race dedicated to the arts of war. The grenade produced total shattering destruction within a limited area of impact. Phillips was standing very close. Even if they ran, he could still throw the grenade. His thumb was resting on the button . . . The Doctor knew that he was literally talking for their lives.

67

'Professor Phillips,' he said again, 'you must listen. You are about to commit murder.'

Something in the incisive voice penetrated to the lower, unhypnotised levels of Phillips' brain. Life had been little more than a blur for him, ever since the Master had kidnapped him from the Research Centre. He had been taken because the Master needed a slave of superior intellect, to service the many functions of his TARDIS. Most of Phillips' time had been spent inside that strange control room, carrying out a variety of tasks according to the Master's instructions. The rest he had spent as a circus clown, stumbling about in the ring with the others, accepting the buckets of water and the blows and kicks without complaint. It had amused the Master to degrade a brilliant scientist into a mindless buffoon. Under the influence of the Master's hypnotic power, Phillips had almost forgotten who or what he was. His nightmarish existence seemed to have gone on forever. But now a voice was reminding him. It was important that he listened so that he could understand what had happened to him. 'The Master is controlling your mind,' the voice was saying. 'You can resist him. You must resist him.'

Part of Phillips desperately wanted to obey the voice. But the power of the Master's mind still held him in its grip. 'You are Professor Phillips,' the voice went on. 'You are an eminent scientist.' Then he seemed to hear the master. 'You will obey, Phillips. You must destroy them.'

To Phillips' horror, his right arm seemed to take on a life of its own. Slowly it raised itself, drawing the grenade back for the throw. His thumb came down on the button . . .

The Doctor grabbed Jo and threw her to the ground. Phillips suddenly turned, broke into a staggering run and threw the grenade with all his force, *away* from the Doctor, and into a clump of trees. His real self had triumphed, but only at the last moment.

There was a dull, heavy 'whump!' The little clump of trees glowed white hot and disintegrated into smoking white ash. Caught by the outer edge of the blast, Phillips was thrown to the ground, killed instantly. Jo and the Doctor, flat on their faces, felt a fierce blast of heat sweep over them.

Cautiously they got up. There were shouts and screams coming from the fairground. People began running towards the smoking circle of ash where the trees had once stood. The Doctor caught Jo by the hand and dragged her to her feet. 'Come on, there's not much time.' Phillips had left the door to the Master's horse-box open.

'Jo, you keep watch,' said the Doctor, and he disappeared inside. Jo looked round anxiously.

There was now quite a little crowd in the area of the explosion, centring around the body of Phillips. She could hear angry voices arguing about what had happened. Heads were turned in her direction . . .

Not far away, Captain Yates stopped the UNIT jeep on the brow of a little hill. The Brigadier sat beside him. Sergeant Benton and a couple of heavily armed soldiers were crowded into the back.

'That's the place, sir,' said Yates, pointing down to the field. 'And look – something's going on. Smoke from an explosion. There's quite a crowd gathering.'

As he spoke, a police car, siren screaming, shot past them and turned into the circus field.

'Better get down there,' snapped the Brigadier. Yates started the jeep and drove down the hill after the police car.

Inside the Master's TARDIS, the Doctor had taken out a panel in the central control console, and was carefully removing a small, self-contained circuit. He heard Jo's voice from outside. 'Doctor, *please* come out!' He lifted the circuit free, and looked at it in satisfaction. It was a fragile-looking assembly of wires and plastic, rather resembling a sort of electronic spider's web. It was in fact a dematerialisation circuit of the kind which the Doctor had been frantically trying to repair on his own TARDIS. He slipped the circuit carefully into his pocket, and went outside.

Jo had retreated to the steps of the horse-box. Surrounding her was an angry mob, led by Rossini. As the Doctor appeared a roar went up from the crowd. 'There he is,' said Rossini. 'Get him, boys. Tried to blow up my safe and steal your pay, he did. Blew up one of my mates with his rotten gelignite.

It wasn't a very convincing story, but the angry roars from the roustabouts made it clear that they believed it. They began to close in on the Doctor menacingly.

Many of them carried mallets, stakes and lengths of heavy chain. 'Listen to me,' the Doctor shouted. 'This man is lying! He's the criminal, not me!'

The crowd started to rush him. Jo pressed herself back against the horse-box in terror. Suddenly there came the welcome blare of a police siren.

A police car skidded to a halt beside them. Two burly blue-clad figures jumped out, and bundled the Doctor and Jo into the back of the car. The policemen jumped into the front seats and the car accelerated away.

It shot out of the field and sped away down the road, just as the UNIT jeep arrived. Yates turned excitedly to the Brigadier. 'Did you see, sir? That was the Doctor and Jo Grant sitting in the back.'

The Brigadier sighed. 'Well, at least they'll be safe enough there. Better get after them. We'll probably have to bail them out.' The jeep turned round and followed the police car, which was now almost out of sight.

In the back seat, Jo Grant breathed a sigh of relief, hardly able to believe that they were safe. Beside her the Doctor was feeling inside his coat, an anguished expression on his face.

'You haven't broken something?' Jo asked.

The Doctor produced the Master's dematerialisation circuit, and sighed with relief. 'No,' he said happily, 'there doesn't seem to be any damage.' He put the circuit carefully away, and leaned forward. 'Good job you chaps turned up when you did.'

'I'll say,' agreed Jo fervently. 'We might have been lynched. Did the Brigadier send you?'

There was no reply from the two broad backs in front of them.

'I hope we're not being arrested,' whispered Jo. 'They don't seem very friendly.'

The Doctor sat back thoughtfully, rubbing his chin. Why would Lethbridge-Stewart have sent the police anyway? He'd have sent UNIT troops, or more likely come down himself. He looked out of the window. They were on a fairly wild stretch of wooded country now. And they were driving away from Tarminster.

The Doctor leaned forward, and tapped the non-driving policeman on the shoulder. 'Perhaps I should explain that we are both members of UNIT, a Government Security Organisation. We were at the circus on official business. I should like to see your identification, please.' There was no reply, and the Doctor tapped on the shoulder even harder. It felt curiously solid . . .

The policeman swung round and looked at him. The Doctor peered closely into the policeman's face. It was a stolid, beefy, rather immobile face. Almost too immobile. Suddenly the Doctor grabbed the policeman's ear and yanked with all his force. The policeman's face peeled away in his hand. There was another 'face' underneath, crude, lumpy and unfinished, like a shop window-dummy left out in the sun. The Doctor's worst fears were confirmed. He was looking into the face of an Auton.

71

The policeman's face peeled away in his hand.

7

The Battle in the Forest

The Doctor reacted instantly. He lunged forward, grabbed the steering wheel from the other policeman and wrenched it savagely to the left. The car lurched off the road and into the ditch. Before it had even stopped moving, the Doctor had opened the rear door, and yanked Jo out and on to her feet. They set off running hand-in-hand through the woods, away from the car.

The impact had jammed the front door of the car, giving them a few minutes' start. The Auton policemen smashed their way out of the wreck, tearing the car door off its hinges, and set off in pursuit.

The Brigadier's jeep shot round the corner, and skidded to a halt by the wrecked police car. The Brigadier watched in astonishment as the two policemen chased Jo and the Doctor. What the blazes was going on? The Brigadier saw one of the policemen stop running, and extend his arm stiffly. The hand dropped away from the wrist on a kind of hinged joint, revealing a tube, like the nozzle of a gun. A sizzling bolt of energy whizzed across the forest, striking a tree branch inches from the Doctor's head. The branch was blasted into flaming ash. The Doctor and Jo ran on.

The Brigadier turned to his men. 'Those policemen are Autons,' he yelled. 'Come on!' He ran after the Autons, followed by Benton, Yates and the soldiers. Benton and the two soldiers were armed with heavy anti-tank rifles, while Yates and the Brigadier had pouches of grenades. Since his previous battle with the Autons the Brigadier had issued standing orders that grenades and light artillery were to be issued whenever there was any prospect of encountering them again. He knew from bitter experience that bullets were useless. You had to blow the creatures to bits to stop them.

Jo stumbled desperately on after the Doctor, but her steps slowed more and more, until the Doctor was virtually dragging her.

'No good,' she panted. 'Can't run, any more. Leave me ...'

The Doctor made a final desperate sprint for the shelter of a fallen tree in a little clearing. He and Jo flattened themselves behind it, trying to burrow into the very ground.

At the edge of the clearing, the two Autons appeared. They paused, wrist guns extended, heads turning to and fro, questing like hunting dogs.

Jo and the Doctor flattened themselves harder against the ground, not daring to move, scarcely breathing. The Autons began to move forward.

The Doctor prepared for a last desperate sprint. Perhaps he could lead them away from Jo. Then he heard the solid 'crump' of an anti-tank rifle, and the crack of exploding grenades. The Brigadier and his men ran into the clearing, pouring a hail of fire at the two Autons.

One of the Autons was hit by shots from the anti-tank rifles and blasted to the ground. Yates and the Brigadier followed up with grenades, and it disintegrated in a shower of plastic fragments. The second Auton blasted down one of the UNIT riflemen, and dodged behind the trees, still firing. An energy bolt whizzed into a tree close to the Brigadier. 'Doctor, Miss Grant! Back to the jeep!' he yelled. 'We'll cover you.'

The Doctor dragged Jo to her feet and pulled her back towards the road. As they stumbled along, they could hear the rattle of shots and the sizzling of Auton energy-bolts behind them.

The second Auton ducked and dodged behind the sheltering tree trunks, returning fire whenever it got a chance.

74

'We could outflank it, sir,' yelled Yates, hurling another grenade. The Brigadier shook his head. 'Pull back,' he ordered.

The UNIT troops began to retreat, still blazing away at the Auton whenever they caught a glimpse of it. Finally it turned and ran into the forest.

The Brigadier, Yates, Benton, and the surviving soldier sprinted back to the jeep. Jo and the Doctor were already inside. Yates took the wheel and they all piled in as best they could.

Jo was shaking with terror, and the Doctor gave her a consoling hug. 'All right, Jo,' he shouted, 'we're safe now.'

But the Doctor spoke too soon. They rounded a bend in the road and came to a bridge over a deep railway cutting. In the middle of the bridge, the Auton was standing waiting for them. It had cut off their retreat.

The Auton raised its wrist-gun to fire. Yates swerved the jeep wildly, then swung it round in a semi-circle, driving straight at the Auton. The bonnet of the jeep struck it in the side with a solid thump. The Auton cartwheeled through the air and disappeared over the side of the bridge. Yates jammed on the brakes and skidded the jeep to a halt.

For a moment the little party sat in a stunned silence. Then they all climbed out of the jeep and looked over the wall. Thirty feet below the Auton lay sprawled over the railway tracks. Yates looked down at the crumpled figure.

'That's settled *him*,' he said with grim satisfaction.

'Don't be too sure,' said the Doctor quietly. To their horror they saw the Auton scramble to its feet and start climbing the embankment towards them. They all piled back in the jeep, and Yates drove at top speed. Jo kept on looking over her shoulder. She didn't feel really safe until they were back inside UNIT H.Q.

*   *   *   *   *

Rex Farrel tapped lightly on the door of the room that had once been his own office.

The Master's deep voice said, 'Come,' and Rex entered nervously. The Master was sitting behind the big desk, working at a pile of papers. 'The schedules are fully worked out now,' he said. 'We are almost ready to leave. All the warehouses are fully stocked and ready to begin work.'

He noticed that Rex was hovering nervously, unable to speak. The Master was in one of his moods of rare amiability. All his plans were coming to a head now, and he was relaxed and confident. He smiled at Rex. 'Well, what is it?'

Rex blurted out his bad news. 'Only one Auton has returned, *without* the Doctor. He was rescued by UNIT. The other Auton was destroyed.'

'A pity,' said the Master lightly. 'But we have many more.'

Rex looked at him in amazement.'You're not angry?'

'Because the Doctor has escaped? Of course not. He's an interesting adversary. All it means is that the game can be prolonged a little.'

'But you still wish to destroy him?'

The Master sighed regretfully. 'I'm afraid it will be necessary, in the end. The more he struggles to postpone his death, the greater will be the final satisfaction.'

The Master passed over the pile of papers. 'Here are the final arrangements for the tour. They are to be made operational at once. See to it, please.'

Rex took the papers and left the office. As soon as he was gone, the Master's face twisted with rage. He slammed his fist onto the desk, cracking the heavy mahogany top. To preserve his enormous vanity, he was forced to pretend that his attempts to kill the Doctor were merely an amusing game, which he could end when he pleased. But each successive defeat was a cause of bitter anger. He began to plan the Doctor's destruction once more. 'This time, Doctor,' he muttered savagely, 'this time you shall not escape me. I shall deal with you myself.'

*   *   *   *   *

Unaware of the Master's plans for him—though they wouldn't have surprised him in the least—the Doctor was sitting in his laboratory checking over the Master's dematerialisation circuit. He was *supposed* to be listening to the Brigadier, who had decided that it was time that a little military order and discipline was brought into things. He had called a conference.

Captain Yates, Sergeant Benton, and Jo Grant sat listening obediently as the Brigadier launched into a full scale appreciation of the situation, in the proper military manner.

'One,' said the Brigadier happily, 'the Nestenes have landed a small bridgehead force. Two, they are operating from somewhere in this area. Three, they are being led by an intelligent and hostile alien, known only as "the Master". Four, to date their operations have been directed primarily at UNIT, and in particular at the Doctor here.'

The Brigadier glanced at the Doctor as he spoke and was not pleased to find him fiddling absorbedly with some piece of electronic nonsense. 'What are you doing, Doctor?' he snapped irritably.

The Doctor looked up innocently. 'Nothing, old chap, nothing at all. Do go on, don't mind me. It's all most interesting.'

The Brigadier gave him a stern look, realised he had lost the thread, and said, 'Where was I?'

'Five?' said Jo helpfully.

The Brigadier cleared his throat. 'Ah yes. Five—the enemy's intentions—'

'Are to invade and occupy your planet.' The Doctor spoke without looking up.

The Brigadier controlled himself. 'Exactly so. Now, to do this, they will at some point have to land additional forces.'

'Obviously.' This was the Doctor once more.

'We have raided the circus,' said the Brigadier through clenched teeth. 'We have arrested Rossini and his thugs, from whom we learned...'

'Absolutely nothing of importance.' The Doctor rose as he spoke, and started wandering restlessly round the laboratory. 'Rossini was a tool, discarded when he was no longer useful.'

'So it would seem,' said the Brigadier. 'This mysterious horse-box had vanished. So had the Auton when we searched the woods. The police car had been stolen earlier.'

The Doctor nodded. 'I imagine the Auton drove the horse-box back to the Master's hiding place. Have you finished yet?'

With icy dignity, the Brigadier proceeded to his summing up. 'I propose therefore to increase our security here at H.Q., and concentrate on finding the Master!'

He looked round triumphantly, as if hoping for applause.

The Doctor sighed. 'Well, now you've reached that brilliant conclusion, how about getting on with it?'

The Brigadier tucked his swagger stick under his arm. Ignoring the Doctor he said, 'Captain Yates, Sergeant Benton, we shall continue this conference in my office.'

Stiffly he marched off. Yates and Benton sprang to their feet and followed him.

As the sound of marching feet died away down the corridor, the Doctor said, 'You know, Jo, I sometimes think the term Military Intelligence is a contradiction in terms.'

Jo looked at him reproachfully. 'You weren't very polite, you know, Doctor. They did save our lives.'

The Doctor did his best to look sorry. 'I'll apologise later, Jo—if I remember.' He picked up the electronic circuit he had been fiddling with and headed for the TARDIS.

Jo looked at him suspiciously. 'What are you up to now?'

The Doctor looked a little shifty.

'Just popping into the TARDIS,' he said vaguely. 'One or two tests, you know.' He disappeared inside the police box.

For a moment there was silence. Then there came a muffled bang from inside the TARDIS. The door opened, emitting first a cloud of black smoke, and then the Doctor. His eyebrows were singed and he was in a very bad temper. Jo opened a window, thumped the Doctor on the back, and gave him a glass of water.

'Come on,' she said sternly, 'what were you up to?'

The Doctor looked shamefaced. He held out his left hand. 'Here,' he said, 'is the dematerialisation circuit from *my* TARDIS. You may remember I was trying to get it going when we first met.'

'Before I squirted it with the fire extinguisher?'

'Exactly.' The Doctor held out his right hand. '*Here* is another and very similar dematerialisation circuit which I removed from the Master's TARDIS. It occurred to me that if I substituted *his* working circuit for *my* non-working one...'

'You might be able to slope off in your TARDIS and leave us,' said Jo indignantly. She was always a little hurt when the Doctor talked about going away again.

'Not until all this business was cleared up,' the Doctor protested. 'After that, I've a right to go if I like.'

'Anyway,' said Jo, 'I gather your little plan didn't work?'

'No,' said the Doctor gloomily. 'You see my TARDIS is one of the original Mark One's. Splendid old machine, mind you. Don't build 'em like that any more. But the Master's is one of these flashy Mark Two jobs. The two circuits just aren't interchangeable.'

Suddenly the Doctor began to laugh.

'What is it?' Jo asked.

'Well,' said the Doctor gleefully, 'my TARDIS may not be working, but neither is the Master's—now. Wherever he is, he's trapped!'

*   *   *   *   *

Unaware that he was now sharing the Doctor's exile for a while, the Master stood in the yard of Rex Farrel's factory. He was watching his Autons loading packing case after packing case into the boot of an enormous coach— the kind that takes tourists round Europe. Inside the coach more Autons sat motionless in their seats. Rex came up to the Master. He was carrying a plastic daffodil in his hand. The Master's black-gloved hand flashed out and knocked it to the floor. 'Careful, my dear boy, we'd hate to lose you.'

Rex cringed. 'I was only admiring the workmanship. It's a brilliant piece of design.' Already he had learned that the Master was by no means immune to a little flattery.

The Master shook his head in a gesture of mock modesty. 'A mere nothing. It was the technology of your factory that produced the finished result.'

An Auton came out of the factory and approached them. Farrel stepped back. He hated to be near the Autons. This one was more frightening than most, for it was a kind of leader. Its features were more finished than the others, and it could almost pass for human. It could speak, too, in a flat dead voice. 'All is ready,' it said. 'We should leave now.' The Master nodded. 'You heard, Rex.'

Reluctantly Rex got behind the wheel of the coach, and drove out of the yard.

The Master's TARDIS, now a horse-box of a different colour, was parked nearby. The Master got in and drove off after the coach.

During the following few days, in suburbs, towns and villages all over England, yet another advertising and promotional campaign got under way. A big gleaming coach would draw up at some central point, and a group of grotesque figures would descend from it.

They wore baggy white flannels, gaily striped blazers, and ridiculous little boaters, perched on giant, grinning carnival heads. They looked both comic and sinister.

In their hands, they held enormous bunches of plastic daffodils. They didn't speak, they gave out no advertising pamphlets, they demanded no box tops, and they made no attempt to sell anything. All they did was give away artificial flowers, just one to each person, to anyone who would accept them. And what flowers! The delicacy of the yellow petals, the green of the leaves and stems, not only equalled but surpassed the colours and textures of the real thing. The flowers became famous. Every housewife in the country wanted not just one, but a whole bunch.

Around each giveaway flower was wrapped a little slip of paper. It gave the address of a local warehouse. If you wanted more flowers you need only write and ask. There was no limit to the number you could order, and only a very small charge for postage and packing. Orders flowed into the warehouses. Thousands upon thousands of the flowers were despatched to homes all over the country. Soon it seemed that every home in the country had its bowl of beautiful, brightly coloured, everlasting flowers.

Exactly what the point of it all was, no one seemed to

know. There were rumours that soon the flowers would be put on the market at an enormous price. People laughed and said they were giving away so many they'd have none left to sell, and nobody who needed to buy them. Nobody really worried. The public was getting something for nothing, and you can't complain about that.

Only the Master, and the Autons, knew that this particular something-for-nothing was the deadly prelude to the second Auton invasion.

8

The Killer Doll Attacks

The Doctor leafed through the batch of reports with ever-increasing disgust. As he finished the last one, he tossed the whole bundle over his head like confetti.

'Worthless,' he muttered. 'Absolutely worthless.'

'They still haven't found the right factory?' asked Jo.

The Doctor shook his head. 'They had one very hot prospect, apparently, then the wretched place closed down.'

The Brigadier wandered into the laboratory, his face filled with despair. 'Doctor, have you seen the latest reports—' He stopped short, seeing the litter of papers over the floor. 'I see you have. Well, I can't say I blame you. We'll have to raid every place Miss Grant visited, Doctor. Only way.'

'Unless we pick the right place to raid first time,' the Doctor pointed out, 'word will get round and the Master will know we're coming.'

The Brigadier nodded gloomily. 'To cap it all, something else has cropped up we've been asked to look into it.'

'Ridiculous,' snapped the Doctor. 'We need all our resources to deal with the Nestenes. We can't possibly take on anything else.'

'It's a pretty serious business, Doctor. A wave of mystery deaths, all over the country. Several hundreds of them so far.'

Despite his preoccupation, the Doctor's scientific curiousity was aroused.

'Don't they have *any* idea of the cause?'

The Brigadier opened the file under his arm. 'Asphyxiation, heart-failure, shock—take your pick, Doctor.'

'Any connection between the victims?'

'None at all. Different ages, sexes, occupations . . .'

The Doctor frowned. 'Anything outstanding about any of them?'

The Brigadier shook his head. 'Don't think so—except that the first one happened several days before the others. Chap had just retired.'

'Poor man,' said Jo. Then for no particular reason she asked, 'What did he do?'

The Brigadier checked his list. A note of excitement came into his voice. 'He used to be the manager of a plastics factory—look!'

The Doctor looked at the list and said suddenly, 'That's one of the places Jo visited!' He began to scrabble about on the floor, looking for the appropriate report. 'Here it is. It's the one I told you about, Jo. The one that closed down.'

'I'll raid it at once,' said the Brigadier determinedly.

The Doctor shook his head. 'Keep an eye on it by all means, but don't raid it. Not until we've had a word with Mrs. Farrel.'

*　　*　　*　　*　　*

By now Mrs. Farrel had managed to come to come to terms with her grief. She managed to put up a good front, though she felt that, without her husband, life was as empty as the big house she lived in.

She received her visitors from UNIT calmly, a quiet little woman in a black dress. She offered them coffee and cake and made polite conversation. She could feel a sort of suppressed excitement in all of them, the young girl, the soldier, and the tall white-haired man in the cloak, who seemed to be in charge. He was a strange, outlandish figure, but there was something very reassuring about him.

With the help of a little prompting, she told them of the events at the factory on the day of her husband's death. She told them of the strange behaviour of their son Rex, after the arrival of the mysterious Colonel Masters. All three of her visitors reacted to the name.

'Do you know what's happening at the factory at the moment?' asked the Brigadier.

'Not really. Rex didn't even come to the funeral. When I tried to contact him, they told me the factory was closed for a while, and he was away on some kind of business trip. I suppose I should have followed it up, but with all that's happened . . .'

The Doctor nodded understandingly. 'I'm going to ask you something that may sound very strange,' he said gently. 'Was there anything that happened at the time of your husband's death that was odd. Something that you perhaps haven't told anybody—in case they didn't believe you?'

For a strange moment she wondered if he was reading her mind. Time and time again, that terrible moment of her husband's death had come back to her. Time and time again, she had seen that ugly shape scuttling away from his body.

'There was this doll,' she said hesitantly. 'Colonel Masters gave it to him.' She recounted the strange business of the ugly plastic doll, which Colonel Masters had apparently pressed upon her husband, and of the fleeting picture that still haunted her of its scuttling away from his body. 'I found the doll afterwards, behind the curtains. But of course, it couldn't move. It was just a doll. I must have imagined it.'

'Tell me, Mrs. Farrel, what did you do with the doll?' His voice was calm, but again she could sense the suppressed excitement.

'I put it back in its box and threw it in the cellar. I'll get it for you.'

It was cold and dark in the cellar, and it took her some time to find the box where it had landed in a dark corner. They were all waiting anxiously when she got back to the sitting room. 'Here you are,' she said.

The Doctor took the box and opened it. The others crowded round. 'I shall have to ask you to let me keep this,' said the Brigadier. 'If you'd like me to issue an official receipt . . .'

She shook her head. 'Take it, please. I never want to see it again.'

She saw them out, and the Doctor paused by the door. 'I know it's little consolation, Mrs. Farrel, but your husband's death wasn't entirely in vain. He was one of the first casualties in a sort of war. What you've told us tonight may help to prevent many more deaths.' . . .

*   *   *   *   *

Captain Yates stuck his head into the laboratory and called, 'Doctor?' He broke off as he saw an overalled figure busy in the corner. 'Hullo,' he said, 'what's going on?'

The man spoke without looking up. 'Telephone mechanic, sir. Just finishing.'

'What was wrong with the phone?'

The man sighed. 'Nothing *wrong* with it. Gentleman

ordered a specially long flex. Says he likes to walk about a bit while he's talking.'

Yates grinned. 'Yes, that sounds like the Doctor.'

The engineer packed away his tools and prepared to leave. 'Got your pass?' asked Yates suddenly.

The man sighed. 'Have a heart, guv. I've had this pass checked so much it's worn to a frazzle.'

'Pass!' Yates repeated firmly. The man produced a grubby pass from his overall pocket. Yates examined it. 'That's fine. Thank you very much.'

The man gave him a reproachful look, took back the pass, and went off. Funny little bloke, thought Yates to himself. Wonder why he grew that beard? Still, whiskers are fashionable these days, except in the army. Yates wondered idly what the Brigadier would say if he sprouted a beard. He could try a moustache, though. No regulation about that. It used to be traditional in some regiments . . .

Yates was just about to leave the laboratory, when he heard footsteps outside. The Doctor, the Brigadier, and Jo Grant rushed in, all in a state of great excitement. The Doctor tipped the doll out onto the laboratory bench, and they all gathered round. 'What the blazes is that thing?' asked Yates. Jo explained where it had come from, and what they had learned from Mrs. Farrel. Yates examined the doll with repulsion. 'Ugly looking beast, isn't it?'

The Doctor had fished a sort of scalpel from one of the laboratory drawers, and was making an incision in the doll. Jo shuddered. Somehow it all looked rather gruesome. 'What are you doing, Doctor?' she asked.

'Oh, just poking about,' said the Doctor vaguely. 'You know, this thing appears to be quite solid. I'll have to do a full analysis.'

'Never mind the wretched doll,' protested the Brigadier. 'Let's get busy and raid that factory. We *know* it's the right one now.'

'All in good time, Brigadier.' The Doctor was busy scribbling on a sheet of paper. 'Jo, I need all this equipment, and I need it right away. I want it installed and operational by the time I get back.'

'Back from where?' asked Jo, taking the list.

'The plastics factory, of course!' The Doctor made for the door.

'One moment, please, Doctor,' said the Brigadier firmly. 'May I remind you this is a UNIT operation? Aware as I am of your preference for acting as a one man band, may I point out that the lesson of the events at the circus . . .'

'All right, all right,' said the Doctor testily. 'Come if you're coming. Don't stand there speechifying.'

'What about me sir?' asked Yates eagerly.

'And me,' said Jo. 'I was pretty useful at the circus.'

The Brigadier shook his head. 'Captain Yates, may I remind *you* that you are officer of the day? Miss Grant, the Doctor needs you to procure his equipment.'

'But sir,' said Yates.

'Please Brigadier . . .' said Jo.

The Brigadier shook his head. 'No, I'm not entirely deskbound, you know. I shall accompany the Doctor myself.' And with that the Brigadier made a dignified exit.

The Doctor grinned sympathetically at Jo and Yates. Pausing at the door, he said, 'Whatever you do, don't touch that doll. It may still be potentially dangerous.'

Jo looked at the little creature as it sat on the bench. It seemed to leer evilly at her through slanted eyes. She shuddered. 'Don't worry, Doctor, I won't go anywhere near it.'

*   *   *   *   *

Inside the plastics factory everything was still. The shining automated machines were silent. There came a sudden splintering crack, as an outer door was forced open. The Doctor and the Brigadier stepped inside and looked around. 'Place is deserted,' said the Brigadier. The Doctor nodded. 'Let's take a look around, shall we?'

Cautiously they moved through the empty building. They searched every inch of it and found nothing. It was a factory, and it was indeed deserted. That was all. Their footsteps echoed eerily, and they instinctively kept their voices low. 'Something over here, Doctor,' called the Brigadier. He pointed to a locked door marked 'Research Laboratory.' The Doctor's sonic screwdriver made short work of the lock, and they went inside.

The Doctor examined the strange alien machinery with interest. He seemed fascinated, too, by the coffin-shaped tank in the centre of the room. 'You know, Brigadier,' he said, 'I think we've found the birthplace of the Autons.' The Brigadier looked remarkably un-enthusiastic. 'As long as there aren't any still about,' he said. He had a grenade in his hand and several more in his pockets. The Brigadier was taking no chances.

'Well, whoever or whatever was here, they seem to have gone,' said the Doctor. 'Let's try the offices, eh?'

They crossed the factory floor and climbed a staircase to the administration area. Here, too, everything was silent. Finally, there was only one place left to check, the big office marked 'Rex Farrel, Managing Director.' You could still see where 'John' had been painted out, and 'Rex' painted over it.

This office too was silent and empty. The big desk was completely bare. In the middle of it lay a single plastic daffodil. The Doctor picked it up and examined it. He passed it over to the Brigadier. 'Hang on to that, will you?'

The Brigadier looked puzzled. 'What for?' The Doctor said, 'It's plastic, Brigadier. And anything plastic, any-thing at all, can be, in the Nestene sense of the word, alive.'

The Brigadier snorted. 'Maybe so. But they're not going to conquer the world with plastic daffodils.' He went to the old-fashioned safe that stood in the corner. 'Maybe they left something in here, Doctor. I'll get it blown open, shall I?' The Doctor looked at the safe disparagingly. 'Don't bother. I'll open it for you myself. I can do it in a couple of minutes.'

The Brigadier said nothing, but gave him a look of polite incredulity. The Doctor fished a stethoscope from his pocket, applied it to the safe and started twirling the dial and listening to the click of the tumblers in the lock. Minutes passed. 'Come on, Doctor, give it up,' said the Brigadier.

'Just on the last number,' said the Doctor airily. He spun the dial a few more times, then stepped back with a satisfied smile. He waved the Brigadier towards the safe. With a sceptical look on his face, the Brigadier grasped the handle of the safe, turned it and pulled. He was very surprised when the heavy door swung smoothly open. He was even more surprised to find that inside the safe was an Auton! Its arm whipped up, and the hand dropped away to reveal the gun.

Instinctively, the Brigadier jumped back. Pulling the pin from the grenade in his hand, he lobbed it inside the safe. Instantaneously the Doctor slammed the heavy steel door shut, trapping the Auton's raised arm as he did so.

There was a muffled 'thump' from inside the safe, and the trapped Auton arm dropped to the floor. The Doctor re-locked the safe door and leaned against it, gasping, 'That was a near one!' Suddenly, the Brigadier yelled out in warning.

The severed Auton arm had started lashing about the floor like a wounded snake, spitting out energy bolts. The Doctor sprang clear, grabbed the legs of the massive mahogany topped desk, and in a feat of tremendous strength tipped it completely over, so that it landed upside down on the still-writhing arm, flattening it into immobility.

The Doctor sank into a chair and shuddered. 'Remarkably persistent creatures, aren't they?' he said. The Brigadier mopped his brow. For once he was at a loss for words.

*   *   *   *   *

Jo watched in satisfaction as the last part of the Doctor's equipment was installed. It had been no easy task getting hold of it at such short notice, and she had had to use all her charm on the dour Scottish Corporal who was in charge of Electronic Supplies. But she'd managed it. The Doctor's equipment was ready and waiting for him—if only he'd turn up to use it.

Mike Yates came into the laboratory, just as the technicians were leaving. 'Care for a cup of nice strong army cocoa?' he asked.

'I'd love one. Canteen's closed though, isn't it?'

Mike winked. 'Every good soldier knows how to improvise.' From behind his back he produced an army billy-can, a tin of cocoa, two tin mugs and a tin of condensed milk. 'You haven't lived till you've tasted my special brew.'

Jo watched in admiration as he filled the billy-can at the laboratory sink, and lit a bunsen burner. He rigged up a sort of stand from a couple of laboratory clamps, and perched the billy-can over the flame. The clamps wobbled a bit, and he looked round for something to steady them. He noticed the little plastic devil doll and picked it up. 'There you are, old chap, make yourself useful.' He positioned the doll to lean against the stand as a sort of prop.

Jo started to mix the cocoa in the mugs. 'Where's the sugar?' she asked.

Yates snapped his fingers. 'There's some in the Brig's office. Hang on, back in a jiffy.'

Jo grinned. The solemn Captain Yates was revealing an unexpectedly human side in the absence of his superiors. 'While the cat's away, I suppose,' said Jo to herself. She picked up the doctor's list and began to re-check the spares he'd ordered. 'Scanning molecular structural analyser mark 6.3,' she muttered to herself. 'Lateral rectifier with reverse polarity . . .'

Absorbed on the complicated list, she didn't notice the little devil doll begin to stir. The heat-flow from the bunsen burner seemed to bring it to life. It stood up jerkily, sending the pan of water crashing onto the bench, and knocking over the bunsen burner. Jo jumped at the noise and looked up. The doll was on its feet, stalking along the laboratory bench towards her. As she stood there paralysed with fear, it sprang for her throat . . .

9

The Deadly Daffodils

As Jo screamed and jumped back, she tripped over a stool and crashed to the ground. The fall probably saved her life. The doll shot over her head, crashed into the wall and dropped to the floor. Instantly it scuttled to its feet, and began stalking her again . . .

She scrambled to her feet and backed away. There was no way of escape—the doll was between her and the door. Gradually it backed her into a corner, positioning itself for a second spring . . .

Mike Yates, walking down the corridor with a crumpled paper packet of sugar in his hand, heard Jo's screams. He drew his heavy service revolver and came running.

He reached the laboratory just as the doll jumped for Jo's throat. He made the shot of his life, blasting the doll in mid-air. The impact of the heavy bullet slammed the doll back against the wall, and it dropped against the wainscoting. Steadying his revolver with both hands, Yates pumped five more bullets into the twitching shape. They literally ripped the doll apart, and it disintegrated into a dozen pieces, head, body, arms and legs all flying in different directions. The crash of the heavy revolver was ear-splitting in the laboratory, and the air full of powder-smoke.

Yates took a deep breath, and re-loaded his revolver with shaking hands. He saw with repulsion that all the little bits of the shattered doll were still twitching and jerking with a horrid life. As he watched, they gave a few more spasmodic jerks and lay still.

Yates switched off the upset bunsen burner which was charring a hole in the wooden bench. He turned to Jo, who crouched trembling in a corner. 'All right, love,' he said. 'It's all over now.'

The Doctor and the Brigadier came in at a run. Yates explained what had happened. 'Are you all right, Jo?' asked the Doctor. She nodded shakily. He picked up one of the doll fragments and looked at it in disgust. 'You've put paid to my chances of doing an analysis, young man,' he said to Mike with mock severity. 'Now then, how did all this happen . . . No, don't tell me. I think I can guess!'

The Doctor looked round the laboratory, taking in the two mugs and the tins of cocoa and condensed milk. 'You were going to make cocoa?' he said, outraged. 'In my lab, and on my bunsen burner?'

Yates nodded. 'I'm afraid I used the doll as a sort of prop.' He picked up the clamps and demonstrated what had happened.

'Heat,' said the Doctor suddenly. 'The thing was programmed to be activated by heat. The bunsen burner set it off, then it probably reacted to the body-heat of its victim.'

'The "victim" was very nearly me,' said Jo who had recovered enough to speak. 'Mike saved my life. I'm sorry if we spoiled your experiment!'

The Doctor smiled at her indignation. 'Yes, you did rather,' he said. 'But never mind, we found another clue at the factory, didn't we, Brigadier?'

The Brigadier looked puzzled. 'Did we? Oh yes—one plastic daffodil.' He suddenly felt rather silly holding the thing, and tossed it onto the bench. 'No doubt that will hold all the answers we need.'

The Doctor looked at him quizzically. 'You might well be right, Brigadier. Now, outside the lot of you! I've got work to do.'

He shooed them all out, and then began checking over the electronic scanning equipment. The telephone rang, and with a frown of annoyance the Doctor picked it up. He wondered vaguely why someone had put such a very long flex on the thing. Still, it meant he could carry the phone to the workbench.

'Hullo,' he said. He tucked the phone between chin and shoulder and went on working.

'Hullo, Doctor,' said a familiar voice. It was the Master.

'What the blazes do you want?' snapped the Doctor. 'I've nothing to say to you—unless you want to give yourself up.'

The Master was standing in a telephone box, on an isolated country road. Parked nearby was the coach, full of motionless Autons, Rex Farrel at the wheel. The Master smiled as he heard the Doctor's voice. 'That's no way to talk to an old friend, Doctor.' His own voice hardened. 'I was merely calling to tell you that the game is over. You begin to weary me, and my plan is almost complete.'

'For the last time,' he heard the Doctor say, 'will you tell me what you want? I've got work to do, if you haven't!'

The Master produced a small electronic device, shaped rather like an egg. He laid the telephone receiver down on the little ledge, put the device near it, and pressed a control. The egg began to give out a steady high-pitched 'ping, ping, ping.' The Master opened the door of the phone booth. 'Goodbye, Doctor,' he murmured softly. He left the booth and climbed into the coach, which immediately drove away.

In his laboratory the Doctor was listening to the repeated 'ping' with mounting irritation. 'Hullo, Hullo,' he yelled. 'There seems to be interference on the line.'

Suddenly the long telephone flex came to life. The receiver wrenched itself from his hands, and reared up on the end of the flex, like the head of an angry cobra. The flex whipped forward and wound round the Doctor's throat, tighter and tighter.

The Doctor struggled to free himself, but the flex was coiling around his arms too now. He could feel the pressure on his throat increasing. His vision blurred and consciousness began to slip away.

His life was saved by pure chance. The Brigadier had suddenly realised that he still had no real idea of the Doctor's future plans. He had decided to return to the laboratory and insist on a proper planning conference.

He came through the door just as the Doctor crashed choking to the ground. The Brigadier ripped the flex from the wall and began unwinding it from the Doctor's throat by main force. It was an incredibly difficult job even when the Doctor had got his breath back, and recovered enough to help him. After a long struggle, they got the flex unwound. They stretched it out between them. It coiled and lashed in their hands, and it took all their combined strength to keep it from getting back round the Doctor's

The flex wound round the Doctor's throat

throat. Finally, they shoved it into a big metal canister which had held some of the Doctor's equipment, and jammed the top shut. They could hear the thing thrashing about furiously inside. The Brigadier looked at the wrecked phone and made one of his rare jokes. 'I'm sorry, Doctor, I seem to have cut off your connection!'

*　　　*　　　*　　　*　　　*

The Auton coach sped along the country lane. In the front seat sat the Master, his eyes fixed on the Auton Leader. The Auton was gazing into space. The Master knew that, through the Nestene universal mind, it was in touch with that tiny fragment of Nestene consciousness that activated the telephone flex.

The Auton twitched, and seemed to come alive. Its head swivelled round to face the Master, and it said in its flat, dead voice, 'The Doctor lives. Your plan has failed. We have withdrawn our consciousness.'

In the UNIT laboratory, the telephone cord stopped thrashing about dementedly in its metal prison. It lay quiet and dead. It was just a telephone cord again.

The Master leaned forward and glared at Rex. 'Drive back to the place where I left my TARDIS. I have business to attend to.'

To the Master's rage and astonishment, the Auton Leader said, 'You waste too much time on your feud with the Doctor.'

A spurt of ungovernable rage shook the Master. 'You dare to criticise *me*?'

There was no emotion in the dead Auton voice. It could feel none. Flatly it said, 'I speak for the Nestene High Command. You risk failure in your principle task. Such failure will be punished.'

The Master controlled himself with an effort. It was humiliating for him to depend on the help of these plastic puppets. But he needed them. Soothingly, he said, 'Soon the operation signal will be transmitted. England will be swept by a wave of death. The Nestene assault force will land unopposed. There will be no failure.'

The Auton Leader seemed to accept what he had said. It turned its head to the front. The Master leaned forward to Farrel and hissed, 'You will obey my order.'

Obediently Farrel swung the wheel of the heavy coach.

*   *   *   *   *

With some amusement, Jo watched the Doctor bringing the full resources of his intellect to bear on one solitary plastic daffodil. He didn't seem to be getting anywhere. Held in a metal clamp, the daffodil sat innocently on the bench and defied all his efforts. He stepped back wearily. 'Well, it isn't heat, like the doll. And it doesn't respond to ultra-sonics, like the phone cord. *Or* electricity. I've *got* to find the right stimulus.'

Yates entered and watched the Doctor for a while. He whispered to Jo, 'Seems a lot of fuss about one plastic daffodil.'

The Doctor looked up irritably. 'The fate of your planet may well depend on this daffodil, young man.'

Yates laughed. 'Come on now, Doctor, it's just some kind of advertising stunt, that's all. They're flooding the country with them.'

'Are they now?' said the Doctor, suddenly interested. 'And who might *they* be?'

'I don't really know,' said Yates. 'It's some kind of advertising gimmick. Coach-loads of chaps with funny heads on. They give these things out, and you can write and get more if you want to. My Aunt Ethel's got bunches of the things.'

The Doctor straightened up, rubbing his chin.

'Why wasn't I told about this?' he asked sharply.

'Didn't the Brigadier's agents know?'

Yates shrugged. 'I think I saw a report somewhere. I thought you were interested in factories making armies of Autons, not harmless promotional stunts like this?'

The Doctor snapped, 'I've said time and time again, anything to do with plastic is relevant, anything at all. Listen to me, Captain Yates. I want you to go to the Brigadier. Tell him that coach must be located immediately. He's not to attack, just find it and track it. Tell him to arrange for immediate warnings—radio, TV, press posters, everything—telling people that these daffodils are extremely dangerous. Get them to put them in sealed containers outside their houses for collection.'

Yates looked a little stunned. 'I'll pass on the message, Doctor. But it won't be easy. You're asking for a nationwide operation, just to collect a lot of silly plastic flowers.'

'These silly flowers,' said the Doctor grimly, 'are the main assault weapon in the second Nestene invasion of Earth. Tell the Brigadier that!'

Yates paused on his way out. He looked again at the plastic daffodil. 'That?' he said. 'But why is it so dangerous? What's it supposed to *do*?'

'That,' said Doctor, 'is exactly what I'm trying to find out.'

Shaking his head, Captain Yates went along to the Brigadier's office and passed on the Doctor's message. The Brigadier looked dubious. 'I'll never get authority for a nationwide warning operation. Not unless there's solid evidence that the flowers really are dangerous. As for finding the coach, should be easy enough.'

But in fact, it wasn't. A few phone calls to the civilian police established that the plastic promotion coach with its cargo of jolly daffodil men was currently touring southern England. It was on its way back to London on the last lap of a nationwide tour. But it seemed to have vanished. The Brigadier called in the RAF. Finally the coach was spotted by a helicopter patrol, and the news phoned through to UNIT.

Some time later the Brigadier was unfolding a map in the Doctor's laboratory. 'There it is, Doctor. Hidden in an abandoned quarry there.' The Brigadier jabbed a finger at the map. 'Been there for some time, shows no signs of moving. I've got Benton with a spotter patrol keeping it under observation. And take a look at this. I ordered a photographic reconnaissance. Pictures are being developed now.'

Jo looked at the map. 'That's funny. The quarry is quite close to the Radio Telescope—where it all started.'

Captain Yates hurried in, with a big envelope. 'Here we are, sir. Still wet from the developer.'

He tipped a pile of photographs out onto the bench. They all showed different views of the coach, obviously taken with a telephoto lens. Several of them had been enlarged.

The Doctor leafed through them thoughtfully. 'No sign of the Master . . . but look at the figures in the coach, Brigadier, the stiff way they're sitting. Those are Autons, I'm sure of it.'

Jo picked up an enlarged view of the front window of the coach. 'And look at the driver. There was a picture of him on Mrs. Farrel's mantelpiece. It's her son, Rex.'

'That settles it,' snapped the Brigadier. 'I've been onto the RAF boys—everything's being set up now.'

'What are you going to do, sir?' asked Yates.

'Bomb it,' said the Brigadier briefly. 'In an hour that coach will be scrap iron.'

The Doctor looked at him appalled. 'The military mind at its most scintillating. Faced with a problem—blast it off the face of the Earth.'

'And what do you think we should do, Doctor?' asked the Brigadier.

'Nothing. Keep it under observation until I've worked out the purpose of these flowers.'

'But surely,' said Jo, 'if we destroy the coach, the flowers will become harmless?'

'My dear girl,' said the Doctor, 'how do we know that? They might be activated by the very act of bombing the coach. Are they being collected yet?'

The Brigadier shook his head. 'I'm sorry, Doctor. You say those things are dangerous. But there isn't a scrap of proof, and the Government simply refused to act without it. However, they know the Autons are dangerous, and I have authority to deal with them as I see fit.' With that the Brigadier marched out of the laboratory. 'He could be right, you know, Doctor,' said Jo. 'Maybe we *should* destroy that coach.'

'Perhaps. But we're still acting without knowing the enemy's full potential. I don't like it. *How* long till that bomb strike?'

Yates looked at his watch. 'About 58 minutes, Doctor. I'd better get down to the observation post.'

The Doctor said, 'If I do find what I'm looking for, can I get in touch with you?'

'Yes of course. You can get me on this.' Yates took one of the miniature UNIT walkie-talkies from his pocket and put it on the edge of the bench. The Doctor was already absorbed in his work again. Yates gave Jo a reassuring smile and left. The Doctor worked on for a moment. He looked up and said, 'Fifty-seven minutes, now, Jo. It's not very long.'

*   *   *   *   *

Rex Farrel, grimy and unshaven, stood by the doorway of the coach. All around him stretched a desolate, dusty sandstone quarry, the workings long since exhausted and abandoned. The coach was at the bottom of a deep gully, sandstone cliffs on either side. Rex thought he saw a flash of light glinting from one of the clifftops. The Auton Leader appeared in the doorway beside him. In a flat uninterested voice it said, 'The human soldiers are surrounding us.'

Farrel looked at him in surprise. 'That doesn't worry you?'

The Auton said, 'Our victory is certain now. When the Master returns, we shall begin the final plan.'

*　　　*　　　*　　　*　　　*

Most of the hour had passed now, and the Doctor was working at a furious pace. He had prepared a micro-section of one of the daffodil leaves, processed it in various ways, and converted the results into a photographic slide. He slipped the slide into a projector. 'Now then, Jo, this should tell us something,' he said hopefully. 'I've converted the daffodil's programme pattern into visual symbols.'

The projector flashed a blurred square of light on the laboratory wall. The Doctor adjusted the focus, and the blur resolved itself into a curiously stylised little picture. Two small holes in a textured background, with a larger hole beneath them. Jo blinked at it, and in the way that such pictures often do, it seemed to form a shape.

'Its a face, Doctor,' she said excitedly. 'Or at least, part of one.'

'Exactly, Jo. Nose and mouth.'

'So what does it mean?'

'It's a weapon,' said the Doctor, vehemently. 'I *know* it's a weapon. But how does it work? What triggers it off? Jo, get on to the Brigadier. I want to see if I can persuade him to postone that air-strike. I'm so near to the answer. Even half-an-hour would help.'

Jo didn't think the request stood much chance, but

she reached for the walkie-talkie which was perched on the edge of the bench. Her fingers brushed against it, and it slipped to the floor. Picking it up she operated the call button. All she got was the crackling of radio static. 'I'm sorry, Doctor,' she said, 'I've bust the thing. I'll go and borrow one from—'

'Look, Jo,' the Doctor interrupted on an urgent whisper. 'Look!'

In its clamp the daffodil had suddenly come alive. Its head swung to and fro, as if it were seeking something.

'Short-wave radio,' said the Doctor exultantly. 'You triggered it off with that damaged walkie-talkie.' He paced about the lab, talking almost to himself. 'They'll be planning to set them all off at once. Some immensely powerful signal to blanket the country. A recognition code programmed into the molecular structure . . .'

As he walked up and down, the head of the daffodil swung to and fro. Deep in his train of thought, the Doctor didn't realise that Jo had moved closer and closer to the daffodil, peering at it in fascination. Jo leaned forward to watch as the daffodil followed the Doctor's movements. Suddenly it swung round so that the bell of the flower faced her. It *hissed* . . .

Jo felt a sudden icy coldness on her face. She tried to gasp, and found that she couldn't. Her mouth and nostrils were suddenly sealed tight, as if by an icy, invisible hand. Scrabbling desperately at her face, fighting for breath that wouldn't come, Jo collapsed choking to the floor . . .

10

Prisoners of the Master

The Doctor crossed the laboratory in two long strides, and knelt beside Jo. He tried to lift her, but she kicked and thrashed convulsively. He saw that she couldn't breathe—but why? Some internal seizure? An alien poison that paralysed the lungs? Then he looked more closely. There was something over her lips and nose—an almost invisible seal.

He ran to the chemical locker, and searched amidst the array of bottles for the right solvent. At last he found it. He tipped most of the bottle on to his handkerchief and rushed back to Jo. Swabbing her mouth and nostrils with the chemical-soaked handkerchief, he tugged the seal away from her mouth. Immediately she began to suck in air, in great whooping gasps. Gradually her lungs stopped heaving, and her colour returned to normal. 'What happened, Doctor?' she gasped. 'What was it? I couldn't breathe.'

The Doctor held out his hand. 'Your mouth and nostrils were sealed with this.' Jo saw a filmy piece of colourless plastic, so thin and transparent as to be almost invisible. 'Doesn't look very dangerous, does it? But without oxygen you'd have been unconscious in two minutes, dead in under ten.'

Jo shuddered, thinking of the many tragic accidents caused by carelessness with simple plastic bags. But this was something deliberate, planned ...

'All those people,' she said. 'The mystery deaths we were asked to investigate.'

'Killed by these flowers,' the Doctor confirmed. 'They probably triggered the things off by accident, just as you did. Or maybe some of the flowers were faulty and activated themselves too soon.'

'What about that poor Mr. Farrel?' asked Jo.

'The doll probably works in the same way as the flowers. I expect he was murdered because he was threatening to cause trouble.'

She went to the door. 'I'll find another walkie-talkie and get on to the Brigadier.'

'Tell him we've got all the proof we need now—thanks to you,' said the Doctor. 'I'm sorry we had to get it so painfully.'

Jo managed a smile. 'First the doll, now this. It just doesn't seem to be my day.'

* * * * *

In a cunningly camouflaged hide high above the sandstone quarry, Sergeant Benton was observing the coach through his binoculars. Not that there was anything to observe. Except for the driver, who occasionally walked about a bit, the occupants of the coach just sat there like a lot of dummies. Natural enough, in a way, thought Benton. After all, they *were* a lot of dummies.

A hundred yards behind him, on the road that ran below the sandstone cliff, a UNIT platoon waited 'at ease'. Captain Yates was holding a weapon check. The Brigadier was standing beside the big RT. 'Thank you, Eagle, we are standing by. Out,' said the operator. He looked up at the Brigadier. 'That's it, sir, air strike confirmed. They're preparing for take-off now.'

The Brigadier looked at his watch. 'Well, if the Doctor is going to come up with anything, he'd better get a move on.'

* * * * *

The Doctor examined the little scrap of plastic film in his palm. It seemed to be getting even thinner. 'Now why wasn't this stuff found on the bodies?' he thought. On a sudden impulse he breathed hard on the plastic film.

It crumpled, melted, and vanished. 'Of course. Melted by the victim's dying breath. Very cunning, that. The final touch.'

'Thank you, Doctor,' said a voice behind him. The Doctor whirled round. The Master was standing in the laboratory doorway, covering him with a stubby cobalt-laser gun.

'How on earth did you get in here?' asked the Doctor, in genuine surprise. The Master gave his self-satisfied smile. 'Few doors are closed to me, Doctor, you should know that. A number of UNIT sentries firmly believe that they have just admitted the Prime Minister!' He closed the door behind him, and looked round the laboratory. He nodded towards the plastic daffodil. 'I see you've been working on the Nestene Autojet. My own contribution to their invasion plan.'

'I thought it must be,' said the Doctor calmly. 'It's vicious, complicated, and inefficient—typical of your thinking.'

The Master scowled. 'You make my task easier.'

'You've come to kill me, of course.'

'Of course.'

'Then how about one or two answers first? Quite a few things about your wonderful plan still puzzle me.'

The Master smiled. 'My pleasure. What do you want to know?'

Beneath his apparent calm, the Doctor's mind was racing. He knew the Master would be unable to resist the opportunity to explain his own cleverness. The Doctor was relying on this to buy him time. Moreover, he really did want to know the answers. He wasn't dead yet, and the more he could get out of the Master the better. 'How are these daffodils to be activated?'

'The Nestenes will send the signal. Once they have arrived, I shall open a channel for them, as I did before. We have distributed over a million daffodils. There will be a million deaths—sudden, silent, inexplicable. The country will be thrown into utter panic.'

The Doctor managed to keep the horror and loathing he felt out of his voice. In a tone of polite interest he said, 'And in the confusion, the Nestene invasion force will attack—is that it?'

'Exactly so! In all the chaos and destruction—'

The laboratory door opened and Jo rushed in. 'I couldn't get through. The frequency's all choked up with RAF signals . . .'

Instantly the Master grabbed her. The Doctor flung himself backwards, and started scrabbling amid a pile of electronic parts on the bench.

The Master's voice rang out, 'Doctor! If you're looking for some kind of weapon—don't!'

Slowly the Doctor turned.

The Master held Jo in front of him like a shield, one arm gripping her round the throat. In his other hand, the laser gun was trained steadily on the Doctor.

'Wait, don't shoot,' said the Doctor hurriedly.

'You disappoint me, Doctor. A Time Lord should face death with a certain dignity.'

'If you shoot, you'll never leave this planet.'

The Master paused. 'You're bluffing on an empty hand, Doctor.'

'I never bluff,' said the Doctor with dignity. 'And my hand, as you can see, is not empty. It holds the dematerialisation circuit from your TARDIS. If you fire that laser, I shall crush the circuit as I die. You will be trapped on a planet where you have only enemies.'

The Master turned the laser gun to cover Jo. 'You still under-estimate me. Let me be plain. Unless you hand over that circuit, I shall kill Miss Grant.'

The Doctor knew that the Master, too, never bluffed. He put the circuit down on the bench and stepped back. The Master threw Jo to one side, stepped forward and pocketed the circuit. Never taking his eyes from the Doctor, he raised the laser gun. 'Any last request?'

'You're beaten, anyway,' sobbed Jo. 'The Brigadier's found your Auton friends. He's going to have them bombed to smithereens.'

To her astonishment the Master released her, thrusting her towards the Doctor. Then he stepped back and raised the laser gun to cover them both. 'There's been a change of plan,' said the Master thoughtfully. 'I've decided to let you both live—for just a little longer. Will you come with me please?'

Jo looked at the Doctor. He nodded. They both left the laboratory, the Master close behind them.

* * * * *

The Brigadier and Captain Yates crouched beside Sergeant Benton in the hide. 'Any minute now, sir,' said Benton, looking at his watch.

They heard a distant hum, which grew steadily louder. Yates shaded his eyes and peered upwards. Suddenly he pointed. 'Here they come, sir.' Three tiny silver shapes wheeled far above them, growing larger and larger.

Inside the coach, Rex Farrel heard the sound of the approaching planes. The sound filled him with panic. 'What's happening?'

The Auton leader said, 'The humans are about to attack us.'

Rex looked round wildly. 'Those are planes. They're going to bomb us. We must get away.' . . .

'We must wait for the return of the Master—he is necessary for the plan,' said the Auton leader.

'He isn't coming back,' sobbed Rex. 'He's abandoned us.'

'He was warned that his feud with the Doctor would endanger the plan. The High Command will be gravely displeased.'

Rex laughed hysterically. 'Displeased? Don't you realise? We're *all* going to die. Only you can't die, can you? You were never alive to begin with!'

The fear of death had overcome the Master's conditioning. Rex pushed his way to the door. 'Well, I'm not staying to be killed. I'm going out to surrender.' The arm of the Auton leader flicked out in an almost casual gesture. It took Rex across the body with the impact of an iron bar. He folded almost double, and collapsed unconscious. The Auton leader resumed its waiting.

In the hide, the roar of the approaching jet-fighters was deafening. Yates and the Brigadier were both looking upwards. Only Benton, obedient to his orders, was watching the coach through his binoculars. Suddenly he tapped the Brigadier on the shoulder and pointed. 'Look, sir,' he yelled. His voice was almost drowned by the roar of the approaching planes.

Along the rough track that ran along the bottom of the quarry, a UNIT jeep was speeding. It was driven by the Doctor, Jo Grant sitting beside him. Behind them was the Master. Through the high-powered binoculars Benton could see the stubby silver gun in his hand. 'It must be that Master bloke,' he yelled. 'He's taken them as hostages.' They saw the jeep stop by the coach. The Master thrust Jo and the Doctor inside. 'Get on the RT, Benton,' yelled the Brigadier. 'We've got to stop that air strike.' Benton began pelting down the steep slope.

The Doctor and Jo sat side by side on the back seat of the coach, covered by the Master's gun. The screaming of the jets came closer and closer.

'What do you think, Doctor?' said the Master conversationally. 'Will your military friend cancel the attack?'

'He will if there's time,' said the Doctor, equally calmly. 'But it's always possible that your rather melodramatic arrival was too late.'

'We shall soon know,' said the Master. 'Won't we, Doctor?'

The whole coach was shaking now with the noise of the planes. The Autons sat utterly motionless. The Doctor, the Master and Jo, all waited silently as the shriek of the jets reached an earsplitting crescendo, and the bombers swooped down to attack.

11

The Final Assault

Benton crouched by the RT set shouting, 'Greyhound to Eagle, Abort mission, Abort mission, Abort mission.' He was yelling at the top of his voice.

In the hide, the Brigadier and Yates looked upwards. The jets swooped lower and lower over the quarry. 'Can't they hear him?' muttered the Brigadier frantically. 'Why don't they turn back?' Any moment now the bombs would start dropping.

In the coach, the noise of the jets reached a final terrifying peak, and began to diminish as they completed their pass and flew away. Jo collapsed sobbing into the Doctor's arms. He patted her back soothingly, but his brain was busy with the next move. So too was the Master's...

In the hide, the Brigadier cleared his throat. 'Obvious, really,' he said. 'They'd already committed themselves to the approach. I mean, it probably takes fifty miles to turn one of those things. They *had* to follow through on the pass. They simply didn't drop the bombs. Never anything to worry about.'

'No, sir, of course not,' said Yates solemnly, trying to suppress a grin.

The Brigadier gave him a suspicious look. Sergeant Benton came running up to them, his face one big smile. 'We made it, sir!'

'There's no occasion for rejoicing, Sergeant Benton,' said the Brigadier sharply. 'The Doctor and Miss Grant may be safe—but so is the Master.'

'What now, sir?' asked Yates. 'They'll kill the Doctor and Miss Grant if we attack.'

'For the moment I haven't the faintest notion,' said the Brigadier frankly. 'We'll just have to hope the Doctor comes up with something.'

Jo and the Doctor were being bound hand and foot by a pair of impassive Autons. Jo shrank from the contact of the huge plastic hands, and winced as her bonds were drawn savagely tight. She saw the Master looking down at her. 'I'm afraid they are a bit heavy handed, Miss Grant. I apologise for the discomfort of your last few hours.' Jo said nothing—she held her wrists as far apart as she dared, trying to remember the UNIT escapology course.

The Master noticed Rex, still crumpled in the aisle. 'What happened to him?' asked the Master irritably.

'He became unreliable,' said the Auton leader. 'He is not important. We must continue with the plan.'

'Indeed we must,' said the Master. 'The first thing we must do—'

He broke off, looking at the Doctor. 'No need to burden you with any more unnecessary information, is there?' he said. At a signal from the Master, Autons dragged Jo and the Doctor to the front of the coach and threw them to the floor by the front seat. An Auton stood in the doorway blocking the exit. At the rear of the coach the rest of the Autons and their leader gathered round the Master for a final conference.

The Doctor wriggled himself to a position where his

mouth was close to Jo's ear. 'You remember where we are, Jo? You noticed when we looked at this quarry on the map?'

Jo nodded. 'Close to the Deep Space Research Centre,' she whispered.

'I'm convinced the Master will activate the daffodils from there. We've got to warn the Brigadier.'

The Doctor craned his head to look at the dashboard. 'Good, they've left the ignition on.' He swung his long legs round so that they reached the controls of the coach.

Jo looked alarmed. 'If you're going to try and drive, I want to get out!'

The Doctor grinned. 'Nothing quite so ambitious, Jo.' She saw his foot reach out for the brake pedal. 'I just hope the Brigadier's keeping his eyes open.'

*   *   *   *   *

In his hide, Benton was still watching the coach. He blinked as a flash of light caught his eye. There it was again. There was a kind of pattern. Benton chuckled, 'Well, the cunning old . . .' He groped for a message pad and began to write. The transmission was a long one. When it was over, Benton called over a nearby corporal. 'Take over observation.'

He ran down the hill to the Brigadier, saluted hurriedly and said, 'Message from the Doctor, sir. Flashed over the brake lights in morse.'

The Brigadier read through the message hurriedly. In curt telegraphese it told of the Doctor's discovery of the deadly secret of the daffodils, and went on to give an assessment of the Master's plans. The last sentence read, 'Over one million daffodils distributed. Urgent national warnings issued soonest. Maximum security guard on radio telescope.'

'Well, now we know,' said the Brigadier. 'Sergeant

Benton, take every available man and put a cordon round that Research Centre. Captain Yates, get onto the civil authorities. We've got to get those warnings out . . .'

In the coach the Master's conference was over. He stepped over Jo and the Doctor and slipped into the driving seat. 'I'm going to take you for a ride, Doctor. But I think I'd feel happier if you were a little further from my back.' The Autons grabbed Jo and the Doctor, and dragged them down the aisle and threw them into the back seat.

The Master started the engine and drove off.

Jo struggled frantically with her ropes. She had never been more grateful for her small size. The Auton knots were clumsy and her hands and wrists were so small that she was able to wriggle them to and fro within the bonds. She worked harder and harder, rubbing her wrists raw in the process. Beside her the Doctor was attempting the same task but with less success—his hands and wrists were bigger, and far more effectively tied.

The coach sped down the road towards the Research Centre.

With a final desperate wrench, Jo managed to free one hand, scraping skin from her wrist in the process. Ignoring the pain, she set about freeing her other hand.

'Well done, Jo,' whispered the Doctor.

He wriggled round so that they were back to back, and Jo could work on his bonds without being seen. She tugged desperately at the tight knots, as the coach jolted along the lane. At last the Doctor's hands too came free.

But their troubles were far from over. They were at the back of the coach, with all the Autons barring their way to freedom. The Doctor looked along the aisle. The Autons sat motionless, facing the front. They were still wearing their gay holiday clothes and the big, grinning heads.

'We could try a dash down to the front,' whispered Jo.

'The Master's driving, remember. He could easily block the front door till the Autons got us.'

Jo looked over her shoulder. An emergency hatch was set into the back of the coach. 'What about that way?'

The Doctor shook his head. 'It'd take too long to open. They'd see, and shoot us down. We'll wait for a better chance.'

Their chance was about to arrive. Rex Farrel was slowly recovering consciousness. His body was one big bruise, but in spite of the pain he was full of a savage joy. For the first time in days his mind was clear. Somehow the shock of the threatened bombing attack, and the pain of the blow from the Auton leader had broken the Master's hypnotic conditioning. Once again, Rex Farrel knew who he was, and what had been done to him. Now there was only one thought in his mind—to destroy the Master.

Cautiously Farrel raised his head a little. To his joy, the Master was sitting right in front of him at the wheel of the coach, back turned. He launched himself at the Master, locking an arm round his throat in a choking grip.

The Master was taken completely by surprise. Remorselessly, he forced the choking hands from his throat— Rex's strength was no match for his own. But the distraction of dealing with the attack forced him to let go of the wheel. The coach careered wildly forward on its own, veering from side to side of the road.

At the back of the coach, the Doctor pulled Jo to her feet. All the Autons were milling towards the front, trying to help the Master, jamming into each other in the narrow aisle. 'Now's our chance,' said the Doctor. He grabbed the handle of the emergency exit, and wrenched it down. The door, unused for a long time, refused to open. One of the Autons turned and saw them. It pointed, and its hand dropped away to reveal the wrist-gun . . .

The Doctor kicked savagely at the jammed emergency

door, until it swung open. With the coach still speeding along the lane, he grabbed Jo. They jumped through the open door, just as an energy bolt whizzed over their heads.

Jo saw the road rushing towards her. Instinctively she protected her face with her arms, bent her knees as she hit the road, and rolled over on her shoulder as she'd been taught in UNIT basic training. Even so the thud of the impact smashed all the breath from her body. She rolled over and over, off the road and into the ditch that ran along the side. For a moment she couldn't move. Then forcing herself to get up, she looked down the road. The coach, swaying from side to side, was rocketing along straight through the woods. Jo watched it speeding away from them. It was almost out of sight when suddenly it ran right off the road, and buried itself in the woods with a splintering crash. Jo looked round for the Doctor. He was lying face down a little further along the ditch. She ran to him and shook him. 'Are you all right, Doctor?'

'I'll know better when I stand up,' said a muffled voice. 'If I don't break in two, then I suppose I must be.' Grimy, battered but cheerful, the Doctor staggered to his feet.

'The Autons are stuck in a wood, about half a mile down the road,' said Jo pointing to the distant coach.

'Come on,' said the Doctor. 'Let's find the Brigadier before they get a chance to sort themselves out.' They ran back down the road in the direction they had come. They must have stumbled along for nearly half a mile when, turning a bend, they saw the Brigadier's jeep speeding towards them.

The Brigadier was overjoyed. He slammed on the brakes, jumped out and ran up to them. 'Doctor! Miss Grant,' he said happily, 'managed to bail out, eh? Well done, well done.' He thumped the Doctor affectionately on the shoulder. The Doctor winced. 'Please! Don't *do* that.' He rubbed his shoulder tenderly and said, 'Brigadier, those daffodils . . .'

'All under way,' said the Brigadier reassuringly. 'Nationwide warning and recovery operation, just as you asked for. Once we knew how they worked, we got straight onto the Government. Do you know there was even a bowl of those wretched flowers in the Cabinet room! Really put a rocket under 'em, I can tell you.'

'Will they be able to collect all the daffodils?' asked Jo.

The Brigadier looked a little shame-faced. 'Well, that's the problem. Been a bit of a rush job, you see. Some people don't believe the warnings, don't want to part with the things.'

'There must be people in isolated places, too,' said Jo. 'People who don't read the papers, listen to radio or see television.'

'If you'd listened to me in the first place,' said the Doctor bitterly, 'we'd have gained a good deal of time.'

'*I* listened,' protested the Brigadier. 'The Government refused to move until they saw proof.'

'The main thing is to stop that signal being sent,' said the Doctor. 'Then, collected or not the daffodils will be harmless.'

'Don't worry, Doctor, that's all under way,' said the Brigadier proudly. 'One of our helicopter patrols saw the coach crash. As soon as we had 'em pinpointed, I pulled the troops back from the Research Centre to surround them.'

'You did what?' said the Doctor angrily. 'You mean you've left the radio telescope unprotected?'

The Brigadier looked hurt. 'Still a small squad there, Doctor. But now we've got the enemy bottled up . . .'

'How do we know they'll *stay* bottled up?' The Doctor was furious. 'If one Auton—or worse still if the Master —manages to get through, most of our work will be for nothing. We'd better see what's happening at that coach...'

* * * * *

The Auton leader was gazing out of the window of the coach. 'Human troops have surrounded us. We have failed. The fault is yours. The High Command will punish you.'

The Master was looking at a map. 'I haven't failed yet,' he said grimly. 'These woods border the Research Centre. You must give me covering fire. If I can reach the radio telescope, I can still open the channel for your people.'

The Nestene Auton leader said, 'We will protect you. The channel *must* be opened.'

'Good,' said the Master. 'Here is what you must do...' The line of soldiers stretched right round the coach now. Benton finished checking the cordon and reported to Yates. 'Everyone in position. We've got the thing surrounded, sir. Do we move in?'

Yates looked at the coach. It looked grotesque and unnatural in the woods, surrounded by the wreckage it had made. 'Better wait till the Brigadier arrives.'

Benton looked at the coach. There was no movement. 'Maybe they're all dead,' he said hopefully.

The coach door was suddenly flung open, and a crowd of grotesque, giant-headed figures emerged. The gaily striped blazers and the little boaters contrasted with the ugly wrist-guns projecting from their arms. The Autons began to fan out and move purposefully through the woods. 'We'll have to try and hold them,' said Yates. He raised his head. 'Fire at will,' he yelled.

The little wood resounded with the crackle of gunfire and the whizzing of energy bolts. The UNIT troops were heavily armed, and the Autons were considerably outnumbered. It should have been an easy victory for UNIT but it wasn't. The Autons fought with savage, inhuman ferocity. They were blown up with grenades, exploded by anti-tank guns ripped apart with machine-gun bullets. Yet still they fought on. An Auton wasn't harmless until it was literally destroyed, shattered into tiny fragments.

Soldiers were blasted by wrist-guns, and smashed to the ground by savage chops from the Autons' powerful arms. Severed Auton arms lashed about like dying snakes, spitting death until they too were shot to pieces.

The fight turned into a series of individual battles as, one by one, the Autons were surrounded by UNIT troops and blasted to pieces.

Yates and Benton moved about, directing the battle. 'Don't give up, Sergeant, do they?' yelled Yates, blasting an advancing Auton with a grenade.

Benton pointed with his machine-gun. 'Those have, sir.'

A little group of Autons was retreating through the woods, leaving the fighting to the others.

Yates watched the garishly dressed figures disappearing through the trees. 'Only three or four—mop them up later,' he said, and returned to the battle.

The Brigadier's jeep arrived just as the last Auton was being shot down. Surrounded by troops, reeling from the impact of bullets, it staggered to and fro firing wildly. At last two well-aimed grenades struck it simultaneously and it disintegrated into a shower of plastic fragments.

Suddenly the woods were silent. Shattered, dismembered Autons lay everywhere, looking oddly human and pathetic in their fragments of holiday finery. It looked as if a seaside concert party had been wilfully massacred. Several of the trees were charred and burning from the searing effect of energy bolts.

A number of UNIT soldiers lay still amidst the devastation. UNIT medical orderlies started attending to the wounded. Jo saw the Doctor's expression of horror as he looked at the results of the battle. He sighed, and shook his head wearily, as if sickened by the slaughter.

'Well done, Yates,' said the Brigadier. 'Did you get the lot? What about that Master fellow?'

'No sign of him, sir,' said Yates. 'One unconscious civilian in the coach.' He pointed to where a UNIT medic was looking after Rex Farrel. 'And one or two of the Autons escaped into the woods—I've got a patrol out looking for them now.'

As he spoke, a UNIT soldier ran up, carrying a brightly coloured bundle. 'Did you get them?' snapped Yates.

'No, sir, not yet—but we found these. Thought I'd better let you know right away.' He held out his bundle —the baggy trousers, and garishly striped blazer of an Auton Daffodil Man, wrapped round the hollow carnival head.

'One of those Autons was the Master,' snapped the Doctor. 'He'll be making for the Radio Telescope. Come on, Brigadier. We've got to stop him!'

* * * * *

In the sub-control cabin of the radio telescope the Master's work was almost completed. Once again he had directed the telescope's beam to that remote corner of the galaxy which held the home planet of the Nestenes. He had boosted the telescope to full power, and the little cabin was humming and shaking with energy. Eventually the circuits would burn out, but that was of no account. Long before that the Nestenes would have arrived. They would send the signal to activate the daffodils—the Master hoped that enough would remain uncollected to cause panic.

Hands flat on the throbbing control console, the Master waited, an exultant smile on his lips. He had won after all—a partial victory, but in the end a victory. Perhaps there would still be time to dispose of the Doctor before he left this miserable little planet to its Nestene conquerors.

Suddenly, the throb of energy in the cabin took on a new, more powerful note. The Master smiled. The Nestenes had made contact. As the power build-up went on, it seemed as if the little cabin would shake itself to pieces. The Master reached forward to turn down the power. There was a crackle of energy from the control console that slammed him across the cabin. The Nestenes had taken control. They would tolerate no interference.

As the Brigadier drove to the foot of the radio telescope tower, Jo and the Doctor saw an incredible sight. The tower was lashing about, swaying like a ship's mast in a high wind. A crackle of Nestene energy filled the air. And between the twin antennae of the telescope, something was beginning to appear. Jo peered upwards, straining her eyes. At first she saw only a flickering, ever-changing pool of light. Then she became aware that something was forming and growing inside it. A ghastly, nightmarish shape was becoming ever more solid. 'The Nestenes!' muttered the Doctor beside her. 'We may be too late—they're almost through.'

He jumped from the jeep and ran towards the tower. Jo saw three brightly dressed shapes appear from the woods—the Master's rearguard. 'Look out, Doctor, Autons!' she yelled. The Doctor threw himself flat, and an energy bolt sizzled over his head. Jo and the Brigadier took cover. A second jeep screamed to a halt beside them, holding Captain Yates, Sergeant Benton, and as many UNIT soldiers as had been able to climb in the back.

'More of the lads on the way,' gasped Yates, unslinging his sub-machine-gun.

'Covering fire, please, Captain Yates,' said the Brigadier. 'The Doctor and I are going up the tower.' Jo, forgotten in the excitement, slid right under the jeep for cover and kept her head down.

While his men opened fire upon the remaining Autons,

the Brigadier ran for the tower steps. The Doctor was already on his way up. It was a terrible climb, with the tower swaying to and fro, the metal steps humming and crackling beneath their feet. At last they reached the platform outside the sub-control cabin. The door was locked, and the Brigadier, in no mood for niceties, booted it open. They burst into the cabin which was a bedlam of noise and flickering lights. The Master sat slumped in one corner. He looked up at the Doctor with a smile of triumph. 'You're too late, Doctor. The Nestenes are here. Look!'

He pointed out of the cabin window. The Brigadier recoiled in horror. The thing in the pool of light had become even more solid. It crouched beside the radio telescope tower, dwarfing it, a many-tentacled monster, something between spider, crab, and octopus. At the front of its body a single huge eye glared at them, blazing with alien intelligence and deadly hatred.

The Doctor had seen that terrifying shape before, during the final battle of the first Nestene invasion. But the creature he had destroyed then had been solid and real, made from the same animated plastic as the Autons. This was something far more powerful and dangerous—a creature of pure force and energy. It seemed invulnerable to all attack.

'A premature landing,' yelled the Master. 'Not quite as I'd planned, I'm afraid.'

'Do something, Doctor,' shouted the Brigadier.

'It's still not fully materialised,' said the Doctor. 'If we could shut off the power . . .'

The Master raised his voice over the din in the swaying cabin. 'Too late! They've taken control now.'

'If I could reverse the polarity—while the transfer shift was still open—that would fling them back into space.'

'You'd never do it in time, Doctor,' shouted the Master exultantly.

Something between spider, crab and octopus . . .

'I could do it if you helped me!'

'Why should I help you?' the Master snarled.

The Doctor shouted, 'If we're finished, then you're finished too. The Nestenes will destroy you.'

'Why should they? I helped them to get here.'

The Doctor pointed to the giant, crouching horror beside the tower. 'Do you think that thing will see any difference between you and us? Your plan failed. You didn't fulfil your promises. The first act of the new Nestene rulers will be to execute you.'

The Brigadier decided to take a hand. He drew his revolver.

'That's one reason, said the Brigadier. 'And here's another. If you don't do exactly as the Doctor orders I shall shoot you here and now!'

Clinging to the console to steady himself in the noisy swaying cabin, the Master considered the situation. Relations *had* been a little strained with the Nestenes of late. He remembered the threats of the Auton leader. Perhaps the victorious Nestenes *wouldn't* treat him as a hero after all. Then there was the Brigadier and his revolver. Time Lords are immensely strong and resilient. They can live to an enormous age. They can change their appearance. They have many strange and mysterious powers. But they are not immortal. The bullets from a service revolver at close range would end the Master's life as effectively as they would that of a mere human being. All in all, thought the Master, perhaps it was time to change sides . . .

'Very well, Doctor,' he shouted. 'You'll put in a good word for me?'

'I'll get you a fair trial by the laws of this planet. Now, shall we stop wasting time?'

Keeping the Master covered with his revolver, the Brigadier watched as the two Time Lords went to work, acting in co-operation for perhaps the first time in their very long lives. They moved swiftly and efficiently, their hands playing over the complicated controls like duettists on an organ. At the end of a long and complex series of adjustments, the Doctor stepped back and called, 'Ready?'

The Master nodded.

'Now!' shouted the Doctor.

Both Time Lords operated controls simultaneously. The crackle of power rose to a single, unearthly shriek. An explosion rocked the cabin, and there was a sudden deafening silence.

Crouched underneath her jeep, Jo Grant saw the shimmering energy-monster flicker and vanish. The Autons suddenly collapsed, turning into lifeless plastic dummies. She scrambled from under the jeep, just in time to see a black-clad figure come tearing down the steps and disappear into the trees. She ran up the steps of the tower ...

Half-stunned, ears singing in the sudden, blissful silence, the Brigadier and the Doctor were picking themselves up.

'Congratulations, Doctor,' said the Brigadier. 'Whatever you did, it worked.'

'Of course it worked,' said the Doctor, closing down the power banks. 'Though if it hadn't been for ...'

They looked at each other open-mouthed. 'He's gone,' roared the Brigadier. 'Well, of all the nerve.'

'Come on,' said the Doctor. 'We'd better get after him.'

He opened the door and Jo Grant cannoned into him.

'The Master,' she gasped. 'Running through the woods —towards the coach.'

She stopped to get her breath, but the Doctor and the Brigadier were half-way down the steps already. Groaning, Jo set off after them.

* * * * *

The UNIT medical officer had decided that Rex Farrel was more or less all right since he'd suffered only a glancing blow on the head, and some bruising. Since no one knew who he was, or what to do with him, Rex had been made comfortable on the back seat of the coach. He was dozing fitfully now, eyes half closed.

Someone came into the coach and he opened his eyes, assuming it was the medical officer. Looking down at him, he saw the face he hated most in the world gazing down at him. The nightmare was not over after all!

He tried to sit up, to scream, but the Master pressed him back into his seat. 'You will perform one last service for me—then you will be free.'

The jeep screeched to a halt by the coach, and the Doctor jumped out, followed by the Brigadier and Jo.

The Brigadier drew his revolver. 'He's probably inside. I'd better go in after him.'

The Doctor stopped him. 'Be careful, Brigadier. Even on his own, he's still the most dangerous man you'll ever meet.'

A second jeep, with Yates, Benton and more UNIT soldiers arrived. The Brigadier barked rapid orders, and soon an armed cordon surrounded the coach.

The Brigadier picked up a loud-hailer from the back of one of the jeeps. 'You can't escape, you know. Come out and give yourself up!'

The figure of the Master appeared in the doorway. His face was set and stern. Slowly he raised his hands above his head and walked towards them.

He walked closer and closer to the cordon of soldiers. Suddenly he made a dash at the nearest one, and sent him flying. Ducking and weaving, the black-clad figure began dodging among the trees.

'After him,' yelled the Brigadier. 'He's making for the road. Try to get him alive!'

The Doctor, Jo, the Brigadier and the UNIT soldiers set off after the running figure. He might still have got away but when he reached the road, more UNIT troops returning from the Research Centre, appeared to cut him off. The Master stopped and raised his hands. The troops encircled him, moving ever closer. The Doctor came up to him. 'Now just stop all this nonsense and . . .'

At the sound of the Doctor's voice, the bearded figure whirled round. With amazing speed, one hand flashed under his jacket and came out with a revolver.

The Brigadier's troops were tired and battle-weary. After their struggles with the Autons their nerves were stretched tight.

At the sight of the revolver, they opened fire by instinct. There was a chattering of automatic weapons, and the black-clad figure spun round and fell.

The Brigadier holstered his revolver. 'Well, that's the end of him.'

The Doctor walked up to the body and looked down into the still face. Jo came up beside him. The Master's face seemed strangely mask-like in death. A terrible suspicion began to grow in her mind—and in the Doctor's too. He knelt beside the body, grasped one ear and pulled . . . The 'Master' face peeled away, revealing underneath the face of Rex Farrel. Hypnotised, disguised, and finally sacrificed, he had performed his last service for the Master. Now he was free.

Suddenly the roar of a heavy engine filled the air. The Auton coach, driven at top speed, was heading straight for the little group. They caught a fleeting glimpse of the Master, crouched behind the wheel, then jumped for their lives, as the coach roared past.

For the second time that day, Jo found herself sitting beside the Doctor in a roadside ditch. The Doctor sat up slowly, shaking his head. He gazed after the coach as it rocketed away in a cloud of dust. For a moment, Jo was puzzled by his expression. Then she realised—the Doctor's face held a sort of reluctant admiration.

12

The End of Round One

'We found the *coach* all right,' said the Brigadier. 'Abandoned three miles down the road. No sign of the Master though.'

The Doctor looked up from the laboratory bench where he was making adjustments to a complicated circuit with his sonic screwdriver.

'Of course there wasn't,' he said.

Jo saw the Brigadier's eyebrows raise at the Doctor's impatient tone. Diplomatically she cut in, 'Well, he's probably left Earth by now anyway.'

'Oh no he hasn't,' said the Doctor.

'May I ask how you can be so sure?' enquired the Brigadier stiffly.

The Doctor grinned. 'Because his TARDIS hasn't got its dematerialisation circuit.'

'But it *has*, Doctor,' protested Jo. 'You remember, he got it back, when he kidnapped us here in the laboratory. You put it on that bench there, and he picked it up.'

'He picked up *my* dematerialisation circuit,' said the Doctor. 'I gave him the wrong one.' He beamed at his own cleverness.

'Really, Doctor,' said the Brigadier exasperatedly. 'What did you have to go and do that for? Now we're stuck with him.'

'Then you'll just have to get busy and catch him, won't you?' said the Doctor unsympathetically.

The Brigadier spluttered, 'He could be anywhere. How am I going to find him?'

The Doctor looked up, his face serious. 'I doubt if that

will be necessary. He doesn't have a very forgiving nature, you know. He'll probably come and find me.'

'He'll have another go at killing you,' Jo said.

'Very probably,' the Doctor agreed cheerfully. 'But he hasn't had much luck so far, has he? Don't worry, I can handle him.'

'You know, Doctor,' said Jo suddenly, 'I think you've got a sort of sneaking liking for him.'

The Doctor looked indignant. 'Like him? I can't stand the fellow. He's ruthless. Depraved. Totally evil. In fact, a thoroughly bad lot. Only ...'

'Only what, Doctor?'

The Doctor looked a little sheepish. 'Well, I do sometimes think the cosmos would be a duller place without him. Not that I won't do my best to catch him, I assure you.'

'I should hope so, Doctor,' said the Brigadier. 'I'm going to institute a full-scale search at once. The only place for him is a maximum security prison.'

With that, the Brigadier marched out. The Doctor resumed his work. Jo watched him for a moment. 'What are you fiddling about with that for? It's the wrong circuit. You tried to use it once, and nearly blew yourself up.'

The Doctor looked up. 'It's the wrong circuit for my old TARDIS, Jo. But the principle's the same. It must be ... If I could make some minor adjustments, you see, I might just possibly be able to adapt ...'

His voice died away as he became absorbed in his task. Jo knew that the Doctor would never give up his dream of repairing the TARDIS so he could roam once more through Space and Time as he pleased. But she couldn't help hoping, for her own sake, that he wouldn't succeed just yet.

Quietly she slipped away. The Doctor was left alone in the UNIT laboratory. He looked up at the solid, blue bulk of the grounded TARDIS in the corner behind him. He reached out and patted it affectionately. 'One day, old girl,' he said. 'One day . . .'

With renewed determination he returned to his work.

The story of the Doctor's first encounter with the Autons is told in :
Doctor Who and the Auton Invasion.

Read of further battles between the Doctor and the Master in :
Doctor Who and the Daemons
Doctor Who and the Sea Devils
Doctor Who and the Doomsday Weapon